OLD RED

The Story of a Devon Fox

OLD RED

The Story of a Devon Fox

TREVOR BEER

Illustrations by the author

First published in Great Britain in 2002

British Library Cataloguing-in-Publication Data
A CIP record for this title is available from the British Library

ISBN 1 84114 162 3

HALSGROVE

Halsgrove House
Lower Moor Way
Tiverton, Devon EX16 6SS
Tel: 01884 243242
Fax: 01884 243325
email sales@halsgrove.com
website www.halsgrove.com

Printed and bound in Great Britain by Bookcraft Ltd, Midsomer Norton

Contents

• ◆ •

vixen's scream of warning was cut short as a terrier fastened on her throat and they fell fighting, rolling and snapping beneath the shadows of the four youths. One of these had killed another cub with his black-thorn stick the guns now useless in the fray. The second terrier now found a hold on the vixen and she fell snapping beneath the combined weight and fearsome bites of the two dogs and she too died fighting the onslaught.

The battle ended as abruptly as it had begun, but a minute or so in real time. The dogs were pulled off the once beautiful vixen now lying in the sand, her dulled eyes staring sightlessly at the darkening skies.

For long moments there was silence. Even the wading birds seemed to have ceased their clamour on the shore. The four men appeared abashed as they stared at the scene of carnage.

'Well, that'll save a few sheep, lads,' said one of the shotgun youths breaking the silence with a forced heartiness.

'Aye. A good night's work I reckon, Bill,' said another still struggling to hold his terrier, which suddenly received a clip across the ear and became still and obedient once more.

The youngest youth kicked sand over the vixen then turned and did like-wise to the cubs.

'May's well cover 'em over,' he said, and then, 'eh, there's only three cubs, where's the fourth, there was four.'

They gazed about. There were only three.

'Why one little devil has shoved off! Well I'll be blowed. Shall us let the terriers loose?' He looked questioningly at the others.

'No. Not now. Time to get out of here in case that warden gets back. Anyways it won't last the night, probably wounded or something and gone back into the earth, let's leave it be.'

And so it was that one cub had bolted at the first shot and had rushed straight into a rabbit hole in the nearby hedge bank which had its exit hole in the adjoining field of marsh grasses and dykes. Unhurt, the fear-some sounds of battle had kept him running until he had collapsed breathless beneath an old alder tree leaning over a pool. Here he crawled into a hole formed by the tree's roots and trembling had fallen asleep as is nature's way. He lay warmly on the dead leaves blown by last autumn's winds as the youths with their terriers made their way homeward talking of the night's events.

Moving On

—◆—

The morning sun rose over the Burrows giving its warmth to the sands, telling the rabbits in their holes, the adders hidden in gorse and bramble, the birds and insects, that a new day dawned.

High in the sky the first skylark awake began its incessant song. He was soon joined by others hovering, ascending and descending over their hidden ground nest sites where their mates sat close on clutches of white eggs, each heavily marked at the larger ends with dark and light brown spotting. In the hollow of an alder tree's roots, close to Horsey Marsh, a small form stirred, wide golden-brown eyes surveying the outside world. A tiny grey spider walked across the strands of its delicate silvery web stretched across the tree roots before the young fox's face and beyond; reeds tossed and waved in the slight breeze of a spring morning. A male blackbird scuffed the earth about for insects or a worm, holding his head on one side, seeking for any sound that might mean food, the dark golden-ringed eyes missing nothing as he went by the hiding place of the fox. It was a reassuring sight for the fox who had already learned well the strident alarm calls of blackbirds when being taught how to hunt with his mother, brother and sisters.

The young fox stretched, moving from the alder roots, feeling the spider web tickle his face as the spider ran along his nose to drop quickly back to its tree root lair to begin the task of web-making once more. For a moment the cub tensed as a great grey bird flapped leisurely overhead to glide deeper into the reed beds fringing the pond and dykes where it hunted frogs each morning. The grey heron was one of several which fished and hunted the estuary and surrounding marshes, foxes of no interest to it or its kind.

The young fox was hungry. Some instinct turned his head towards his old lair, and he trotted in that direction leaving a trail of paw prints in a straight line behind him. As he topped a rise in the ground he heard the familiar sound of a vehicle engine and he crouched as his parents had taught him, peering through marram as the vehicle drew nearer and stopped. The warden slammed the Land Rover door and strolled to where he had noticed much trampling in the sand near the road. He stared long and hard at the boot marks and the head of a vixen staring back sightlessly from where she had died defending her cubs. Cursing under his breath at the obvious implications, he brought a shovel from the vehicle and properly buried the foxes, erasing all traces of the night before, even to taking away the spent cartridge cases.

Once again the area had a natural look. The warden sat on the bonnet of his vehicle and surveyed the surrounding dunes through his binocular. A few rabbits about, he noted, and a kestrel hovering over a wet slack which would soon be blue and gold with viper's bugloss and evening primrose flowers. He did not see the young fox as it crouched low above him, nor did he see it turn to leave the Burrows to head back to the denser cover afforded by the marshes. The cub was now on his own, earlier than nature had intended, and with a lesson about mankind indelibly imprinted on his mind.

In the hazy spring sunshine he trotted along a track into the marshes to where a derelict old building seemed to beckon. It was here in the doorway he found the remains of a plump rabbit, which he promptly fell upon, eating ravenously from the fresh meat. The rabbit had been partly eaten by a buzzard hawk, which had killed the animal earlier that morning and eaten its fill. Now the buzzard perched in an oak tree near Marstage Farm, watching the day go by near to where his mate sat on eggs in their large stick nest built safely into the tree fork.

The fox ate until his stomach could take no more and with a deep sigh he curled up on some old sacks and windblown leaves in one corner of the room where it was dark with shadows and fell soundly asleep.

Back on the Burrows

＊

The evening was cool and quietly peaceful after days with little rain, the Burrows alight with the beauty of a June sunset, a faint blush washing the sky pink and gold towards Lundy, the Isle of Puffins. The setting sun lit the westwards-lying dune slopes pale orange as above them a full moon floated pale as a cloud in the violet sky. Purple shadows invaded the steep dune valleys, cooling the sands and sending lizards and adders scuttling and slithering into their night roosting holes. The fox had left the marshes to hunt the dunes where he had been born. He knew well now certain tracks and was passing concrete structures left by war training to gain the beach while the light was good, but on reaching Doughnut Pond paused to drink from the cold fresh water, using the cover of rushes as he did so, watched by the great compound eyes of many dragonflies perched resting after a day of darting and hawking over the water for smaller insects.

As he drank from the little pond with its circular island in the centre a large rabbit hopped onto the path before him. Unseen by the young fox the old buck sniffed the air, his large gleaming eyes rolling as he took in the scents on the breeze, learning from them who was about, then he hopped onward to a clump of marsh bedstraw into an open area of sand, and into the fox's view.

The fox, just at that moment lifting his head from the pool, immediately froze into watchful stillness, the only movement jewel-like droplets of water rolling along his whiskers to drop silently onto the grass at the pool edge. A skylark hurrying to its night roost ran into the shadows beneath the fox's motionless form and through his hind legs, yet still the fox did not move as he watched the lone rabbit move nearer to the water. His mouth watered with his own saliva now as he lowered his head and shoulders, sinking into the sparse cover of a spray of viper's bugloss not yet in flower. He crouched lower, his belly hugging the cool sand, his ears hearing the sounds of human voices and he looked with sudden fear in the direction of the noise. The rabbit also hearing the sounds hopped away and into the hole he had earlier emerged from, scattering sand grains onto the carpet of wild thyme spreading from the burrow entrance.

The fox could now hear soft footfalls coming from the area of grey or fixed dunes some distance from where he remained crouching. He moved away along a huge depression in the sand where, ten years before he was born, a screaming wind had blown out the entire side of a partly fixed dune where even now only sand sedge had recolonised. The fox moved seawards away from the two men and a woman who were busily setting nets over rabbit holes to do some night poaching.

The men were brothers, the descendants of generations of poachers and lived in the nearby market town. Hereabouts they considered themselves as having the right to take game as and when they wished as had their forefathers, long before rules were made to stop them and long before nature reserves were even thought of. As they worked swiftly in the dimming light, the fox padded down over a seaward dune slope to turn north along the beach towards Saunton. A strange and sickly smell invaded his nostrils and the fox snarled, drawing back his ears, moving away from the sea for the stench was strong on the onshore breeze. He moved warily along the dune fringe for a half mile but the stench persisted, making his eyes water and his head hurt. Instinct told him to leave the beach though he could perceive no dangers that he knew. He glanced up over the dunes for a safe place to breach them but the sand was soft and he slid back to the beach to trot along the strandline where he felt a stickiness on one forefoot.

He snarled again, his paw gathering sand grains as he ran. A moving shape loomed before him and the fox swerved to avoid the strange beast, which stank with the smell upon the air. He leapt away from another shape which hopped and fluttered, black and shining, along the sands then finding a gap in the dunes he ran away from the grotesque moving shapes coming in from the sea. The shapes were guillemots and razorbills, birds of the auk family who a few hours before had been swimming and diving for fish out at sea. Miles beyond them on the horizon the grim grey shape of a passing tanker had cast waste oil into the waters, contaminating all in its path. Now, unseen and dying from ingested oil, the birds struggled ashore blind and helpless as each successive wave from the tide flow brought more filth onto the beaches of the Westcountry coast.

The blood-red orb of the setting sun did not light their way ashore for the birds eyes were coated with oil, every stick and stone upon the beach an obstacle as they fell exhausted to the ground to lie prone, awaiting whatever further fate lay in store for them.

The fox, loping swiftly along the beach towards Saunton had splashed through rock pools, which cleaned the offensive substance from his paw.

He paused to eat a crab and with the oil stench behind him he climbed a narrow path to find himself on a grassy cliff-top of springy turf where many ewes and lambs lay chewing contentedly in the last light of day. The fox gazed about him, ignoring the sheep, then followed a track westwards beneath a drystone wall which ran from the cliff edge to the main road between villages. Here he heard the deep throated 'pruck-pruck' of a raven and felt the wingbeats of the bird before he saw its black shape pass him to alight on a broken fence across a chasm in the cliffs. Answering calls came from the raven's mate, the two great black crows settling for the night, the female still using the large stick nest where their young had been raised earlier in the year. She saw the shape of the fox's head loom momentarily as he peered over the cliff edge but her eyes were filled with sleep and the darkness of the night.

The fox moved on, his hurrying feet stepping upon the recently sloughed skin of an adder, which lived in a hole in the stone wall. He wandered up along the field following the wall to where a pile of stones showed a well-used track leading up to a lay-by on the roadside. Squeezing through a tangle of hedge-parsley he stood for a moment by the wall as two pairs of startled eyes gazed from a car parked a few feet from him. The young couple saw him leap down to cross the road and disappear amongst the bracken and gorse on the opposite hill slope. They would talk about the fox sighting many times but he had already forgotten them, the recent meal of a crab only serving to make him the hungrier now and urging him to find a better meal.

A nightjar churred beside him and rose moth-like into the night sky, clapping its wings beneath its body over the spot where its mate lay covering two white eggs hidden under bracken on the ground. The fox ran faster along the hillside track not recognising this strange visitor that arrived on the Westcountry mainland after a journey of many miles across the oceans each year. He ran on through the gardens of a large house where pine trees held the nests of many rooks, then through a chapel garden as the night suddenly became very dark.

Almost immediately the darkness disappeared as a bright moon shone its pale light upon the scene, the clouds obscuring it moving on towards Baggy Point and the villages of Putsborough and Woolacombe. The fox's way was silver-lit now as he leapt at and missed a vole crossing his path but he did not pause until he topped a rise overlooking the pond near Saunton Court house.

He gazed about him but naught moved in the shadows as he followed a steeply narrow path to the pond edge where he heard crunching and snuffling sounds from the reeds about its edges. Warily he raised his head to peer over the sharp dagger-shaped leaves. A hedgehog, disturbed by the fox shadow falling upon it, rolled into a ball beside the nest of a moorhen containing a clutch of six eggs which it had been about to eat. The fox sniffed at the hedgehog but had not learned to roll the animal into the water where it would uncoil to be eaten so he left it and ate two eggs, nipping into the shells with his front teeth and lapping the contents hungrily. He drank from the pond then ate two more eggs before moving on beneath trees to a woodland path where he found the feathers of the female moorhen killed earlier that same evening by a mink, which lived in a hollow tree in the gardens of Saunton Court. Behind him the hedgehog uncurled its spiny body and began to eat the remaining eggs.

Near the road edge the fox waited as a huge noisy creature blazing with lights and human faces stopped then moved on again along the grey ribbon of road. He placed his forepaws upon the stump left by the felling of a dead elm tree, to stare over the hedge after the departing coachload of visitors until it was barely a sound in the direction of the village of Braunton, whereupon he dropped lightly to the now silent roadway following it to where a track led to a small farmhouse and cottages. Here he passed under a sign proclaiming 'Cream Teas' and a brightly lit window from which came the sounds of human voices. Swiftly he ran beneath it, passing outbuildings from which came the smell of horses. Hearing the first pattering of raindrops, he hastened onwards to the outskirts of Braunton.

Where the river ran beneath a road the fox turned through a car park, following the waterway through several gardens where cats spat at him in anger at his intrusion but did not venture into the rain. Leaving the village behind him he came to a ditch near the Great Field where two large rats reared up at his approach, dying as he snapped and shook them from left to right before they knew what was upon them. He bit and ate from one then feeling the rain heavier upon his back he picked up the second rat to trot across the fields to his barn on the marshes.

The warm summer rain was heavy now, large drops pattering upon the Burrows and marshes, pounding the sands and already beginning to wash away the beached black oil that soiled and despoiled them.

Of the Burrows and a Gift

●◆●

In his first days of independence the fox had lost no time learning the ways of a lone fox in the wild, for learning is survival. Of an age when he would still have remained with his mother for some months, he nevertheless learned from necessity the primary objectives of food and his own safety. The vixen had taught the cubs well the first lessons of hunting, of using all available cover when moving across the country-side, and as the first-born cub he had grown strong, with luck on his side on the night of the tragedy that had taken the lives of the vixen and the other cubs.

He had not gone unseen on the marshes. The farmer who owned the land with the derelict barn upon it had observed the young fox several times and admired his bright red coat and oddly grey muzzle that reached to the white of his face and neck. He had called the fox 'Old Red' from this colouring and spoke of him as such to his wife when he recounted the events of the day, having no quarrel with an animal who caused him and his stock no harm.

Now at midsummer when the air was filled with gorse scent, Old Red left his lair; crossing the fields to the cover of a high hedge bank of hawthorn and blackthorn trees, then on along the sea wall to the pond lying still and blue-green close to the White House close by the tidal reaches of the Taw river. For reasons known only to himself, the fox often chose to wander abroad during the last hours of daylight or at dusk.

The green dagger leaves and golden yellow flower heads of flag iris waved in a slight breeze, reflecting deep in the waters of Horsey Mere. The rattling songs of whitethroats and sedge warblers came loud and Old Red heard, too, the reeling calls he knew came from a small brown bird whose mate was incubating eggs in a nearby patch of brambles. The male grasshopper warbler perched atop the tangle of vegetation near the nest, calling his far reaching song into the warm summer evening. Artfully concealed a few inches above the ground within the dense tangle the nest was as safe from predation as any upon the marshes, and safer than most.

Old Red splashed through shallow water at the pond edge, pausing as the incessant reeling suddenly ceased and an oppressive silence fell upon the marsh. He crouched low in the yellow flag as he heard the bird call 'twhit-twhit' in alarm, warning his mate, and then saw it drop into concealment in the vegetation. The fox strained his eyes and ears for signs of danger but none came. He moved up over a steep bank, peering up and down the narrow marsh road but it was traffic-free and silent. The grasshopper warbler returned to his perch and watched the fox disappear over the top of the grassy bank whereupon he began again his reeling song. With his mate on eggs he took no chances and having seen the fox nearby had immediately warned her of impending danger.

Old Red reached the dyke edge where the slow-moving water was bridged from the road by a trackway that ran out over the marshes. He squeezed under a rickety wooden gate to follow another dyke fringed with reeds, pausing to drink until a loud hissing startled him and he sprang back as a female mute swan came gliding rapidly between him and her nest perched just across the dyke.

The fox saw the male swan or cob swimming fast from further along the dyke, the water a bow wave at his breast as he bore down upon the fox who detoured wide of these large white birds as the pen half raised her wings from her back, allowing her three downy grey cygnets to clamber upon her. She joined her mate who raised himself from the water on beating wings defying the fox to return.

Old Red had already forgotten them and ate two earthworms that had become exposed when his paws trod the soft earth at the dyke's edge, which had fallen away to reveal the succulent morsels. The soil fell into the water with the plopping sound of water voles, sending a shoal of small fish darting in zigzags fearing the invader of their peace was a heron or kingfisher. Old Red pawed at more earthworms at the dyke's edge and learned that this was a way of finding food as he watched the bank fall away beneath his scrabbling. He ate another large worm but two others had fallen into the water to wriggle palely as they submerged to the dyke bed, becoming 'ghosts' before his eyes.

Old Red moved on through more yellow flag and purple loosestrife, his feet taking the scent of water mint as he waded in the shallows, jumping nervously as two wood pigeons clattered out of a barn at the water's edge. He pointed his nose inside, seeing several beetles on the mud floor. He ate them, the sun where it shone through the roof timbers of the disused building, warming his glossy red back.

A magpie cackled over him as he left the barn and, joined by another, harassed him along the waterway until he passed by the hawthorn tree where their nest was built. Skilful marauders of the nests of other species, the magpies were equally successful at protecting their own. The fox did not waste his energy on retaliation on these black and white birds whose shining tails showed the colours of rainbows and dragonflies, and he trotted onwards. He heard the squeaking of field voles before him and leapt high, coming down with all four paws close together to feel a squirming form held securely by one foot. The fox held fast, hearing the feeble squeak of the captured vole, and removing his foot he ate swiftly and moved on.

Coming to a stand of sallow the fox heard tapping sounds and moved silently forward to investigate. He watched as a warmly-coloured bird with speckled breast beat a snail against a heavy stone. He watched, head on one side then the other, as the song thrush dashed the snail several times against the stone until the shell split open to reveal the meat within. She ate it, then, with scarcely a look about her, flew to her nest in the sallow where five young were hidden, seeing the fox shape move away below her as she settled. Old Red sniffed at the broken shells and moved on, ignoring the numerous black slugs making their slow way out from the vegetation to forage for the night, for like all foxes he shunned slugs and toads.

Reaching a place known as Southern Flats he passed through an area of small paddock fields alight with buttercups, becoming covered in golden pollen so that his coat shone with yellow lights as he ran. Loud snorting caused him to swerve away from a roofless stone-walled building, and two chestnut horses chased him into the American Road where he ducked beneath barbed-wire fencing to escape into the dunes. He ran across grassy wet slacks, dry now with the low water-table of summertime, reaching Crow Point to find a high spring tide surging heavily almost to the dune bottoms, grasping fingers of water reaching for his feet. He climbed up and away over the fore-dunes, turning again to follow a narrow path running inland parallel with the river. Rabbits ran swiftly before him as an old buck sounded a warning, their own white scuts telling others they were running and thus to get underground away from danger. Old Red chased the buck, nipping a heel as the leader of the warren bolted speedily into a large hole to become lost in the darkness.

The sun dipped and began to sink into the estuary, vast now with the tide flow. Mallard put up before the fox, calling angrily at being disturbed then flying low over the orange water glow to Isley Marshes on the other side of the wide river, using the derelict buildings of a defunct power station as a landmark in the swiftly fading light.

A dark shape loomed before Old Red on the pathway and he halted, crouching, with hackles rising as the scent of rabbit mingled with that of human and unease ran through him. He moved to one side into the cover of gorse which grew thickly here, as moths began to trickle into the gathering night. The dead rabbit shape lay on the path before him, nor was there a sound to alarm him. The human scent faded with the breeze blowing off the estuary. Only river scents now came to his nostrils. A sand barge chugged by and voices from it reassured him for it was a sight and sound he was used to, the barges gathering sand and gravel here as others had done for many years before. Old Red raised his head high sniffing in all directions then moving forward he gathered the carrion into his jaws with watering mouth. A flash of light lit the scene around him and was gone before he could blink but the fox was already on his way homeward with his prize.

He reached a place where tin sheds stood near the pathway used by boatmen and fishermen, then came to a stile and a gate which he ran beneath, dragging hard on his rabbit, to find a deep rutted track leading on to the Toll Road. The sun set as he passed the Toll House, the land starlit and cooling as he reached his lair and settled to eat from the plump doe to the call of barn owls hunting across the marsh fields.

Near the White House a young woman smiled as she strolled homewards happy in the knowledge that the rabbit she had placed out for the fox had been accepted. She felt a bond between them, fragile yet lingering, and with luck the photograph she had just taken by flash light might be a good one. She hummed a tune to herself as she walked, seeing in her mind's eye the brief but exciting moments with the fox, picturing the paintings she would make of the scene.

Not far distant Old Red crouched and crunched happily on rabbit flesh and bones, his own needs fulfilled as he ate and watched the night.

Of Shelduck and Things

⬧◆⬧

One week after the find of rabbit left for him by the young woman, Old Red hunted on yet another warm summer's night when little moved or seemed to want to move on the marshes and the Burrows. He had followed the orchid path from the American Road, his paws occasionally tapping against marsh orchids which grew on stiff stems and did not snap or fall at his passing. The scent of thyme clung to his feet where the deeply pink flowering plant grew as a low carpet around the mouths of silent rabbit burrows. Old Red reached the Flagpole Dune without seeing rabbit or vole in the stillness of the night, though one or two watched him from the seclusion of their lairs.

He licked at a tube containing a sweet, sticky substance but could not get his tongue into its neck where the scent of the issuing liquid was strongest. He licked the sweetness and played with it, tossing his head and leaping about with the bright object, then tiring of the game he left the morsel lying on the sands, moving on, hunger pangs stronger than the urge to play. The tube was of strawberry jam, discarded army rations from recent exercise manoeuvres in the Braunton Burrows Training Area.

Old Red followed a wide trail of footprints left by the soldiers the day before and found himself deeper in the dunes where he came upon holes dug in the ground smelling of human sweat. He left quickly, coming to to a place known as Horsebreakers Slack along the landward side of the dune slopes, and here he came upon a solitary rabbit which had seen his arrival. He chased her at speed, running up and down the steep dunes as the soft, leg-tiring sands rolled gently down beneath their chasing, the fox nipping the hairs from the hind legs of the rabbit as it dashed before him, eyes rolling. Again Old Red tasted fur but with a sudden twist the rabbit was gone, into an old warren hidden in sea buckthorn, leaving the fox panting, staring at the black hole too small to allow him access. He stared hard as if willing the rabbit to return but already it was lying on one side in the darkness of its refuge and would not venture out again until the next evening's light gave it full view over the terrain. The fox moved on amongst sleeping restharrow flowers, trotting in a wide arc across the dunes, pouncing upon dark shadow movement beneath cream-coloured marsh helleborine orchids to find a toad beneath his forepaws which he quickly let go, not liking the taste. He came to a small wet slack where a stand of sallow threw dark shadows across the sands and here, half-way up a dune slope, he heard sounds coming from a large rabbit hole.

Some instinct known only to his kind caused him to move away down the dune where he slipped into cover beneath the sallow shadows, lying with his head upon his forepaws, his eyes fixed intently upon the darkness that was the rabbit hole in the dune slope.

He dozed without knowing that he dozed, the dark hours of the early morning passing into a rising mist, the dawn breaking wanly upon the north Devonshire sea coast. The sun lit the land without shadows as a spider moved across its silken web stretched between carline thistle stems, the strands vibrating, holding quivering beads of mist that shone dully in the pale light. The spider dropped on its silken line and swung down on to the still, furry nose of Old Red who opened his eyes to find the morning. He saw the movement on the end of his nose and wiped a forepaw across it, the spider falling unharmed to the vegetation where it promptly began to search again for its web along the now loosely dangling thread.

Old Red dozed the morning through, remaining in the dune hollow, letting the sun warmth play on his lean body as he lay outstretched, listening to the sounds of birds holding territory nearby, the willow warblers and chiffchaffs from their African haunts, and the several resident species nesting or feeding in whatever vegetation they could find. The sun rose high, bringing a heat haze which caused the dunes to wave and wriggle in the distance as if they were but a mirage. Here common blue butterflies sought pink restharrow flowers and small coppers and skippers chased over the herbage of the wet slacks.

Movement above the fox became a shelduck winging out of the mist veil that had yet to burn off the nearby marshes. Old Red excitedly watched the black, white and chestnut bird slow its wingbeats to glide to the soft ground in the slack hollow and waddle forwards, as it began uttering calls of contact to its mate hidden below ground in the dark recesses of the rabbit hole the fox had investigated earlier.

'Arrk-arrk-arrk' the sheldrake called, pausing at the foot of the dune directly below the hole, and again, 'arrk-arrk' as Old Red heard answering calls. The female's head appeared at the mouth of the burrow and gazed about. For a moment her head disappeared then showed again as the duck left the safety of the disused rabbit burrow and, shaking herself, gazed proudly down upon her mate.

Turning her dark head she called softly 'uggugg-ugg' into the hole as the first of her nine young appeared in view, its soft downy feathers mottled whitish and dark brown. It ran to its mother, promptly followed by the rest of the brood as Old Red rose to his feet, eyes staring, tongue lolling, as he focussed on his next meal. 'Whee-chew, whee-chew,' came the rapid alarm whistles of the drake as he saw the fox on the distant slope then as Old Red loped towards them, 'sank-sank', repeated rapidly as the drake realised his mate and brood were threatened. The shelduck chicks gathered about their mother who, seeing the fox running towards her, gave the alarm calls again as her mate rose almost beneath Old Red's jaws, beating at him with his wings. But the fox was not to be deterred from a meal. He rushed with head low to the female who turned on him with alarm as he passed her, killing two chicks as he did so, feeling the sheldrake's wings beating again at his face as he swerved away and rushed the female. Feathers flew from her breast as she fell to the ground buffeting the fox with failing wingbeats and hearing the shrill piping of her remaining chicks as they streamed along the dune slope into the vast acres of the Burrows after their father, his calls guiding them to the safe waters of an estuary at full tide. Old Red did not see them go, nor did he heed the two dead chicks, for he was already homeward-bound, clasping the heavy weight of the female shelduck in his jaws. She would last him for two days or more during which time he would not have to leave his lair to hunt. For the moment all was well with his world.

Of Cormorants and
Other Foxes

•◆•

In the soft dawn light of a late summer morning when the rising sun struggled to penetrate the dense banks of mist over the estuary, Old Red sat on the sea wall watching duck out on the ebbing waters where the two rivers, the Taw and Torridge, flow together following their long journey from Dartmoor. The fox was not hungry, for the night before he had hunted the dewy grasses of the Great Field, catching and eating voles which he loved and were plentiful. He had dined well and then left the Great Field to wander idly along the track to South Burrows cottage and on to Airy Point, then out along the sea wall to the White House and Horsey Island.

A large black bird with fast-beating wings flew by him heading up river from Baggy Point where it lived with others of its kind along with shags and oystercatchers. The bird was a cormorant, one of several which nested on the sea cliffs to the east and fished the rivers and reservoirs all around. Three more followed, younger birds with much white upon their breasts, striving hard to keep pace with their mother already a hundred wingbeats ahead.

Old Red watched them fade into the mists on black, flapping witch-wings, their long necks outstretched as if eager to reach the food to be found at Wistlandpound Reservoir, their inland destination for today's fishing, where they would dive for fish beyond the shaking fists of human anglers who feel that the fish are their own.

As the paleness of the mist engulfed them, another cormorant alighted on the water before Old Red's gaze to dive beneath the surface. On its fourth dive the bird surfaced with an eel as long as a man's forearm and Old Red watched as it opened wide its gape, the eel wrapped wriggling about it as for long moments they struggled, but still the bird made its way shorewards where it knew it could more easily win the battle. Waddling awkwardly up the beach the cormorant dashed the eel to the ground, pecking at it several times, but the fish would not die, writhing again as the bird gripped it between sharp mandibles before taking its head into its throat and swallowing it whole.

The fox saw the eel disappear, watching the last flick of its tail as it vanished into the bird's gullet which suddenly convulsed, writhing with the contortions of the eel still fighting for its life in the alien blackness of the cormorant's throat. For five minutes more the bird's throat wriggled and jerked from chin to breast, the bird almost losing its footing at times as the fish jerked it off balance, its darkly feathered neck twining as seaweed in the tide currents. Again the cormorant gulped and the eel weakened and died, sliding from the bird's neck to its stomach whereupon the cormorant screamed defiantly once then, opening its black wings, gazed solemnly at the estuary with emerald eyes.

The mist lifted, allowing sunlight to warm the fox, and Old Red saw the first dunlin for the year arrive on rapid wings from their Greenland breeding grounds to land before him. Immediately the birds began stitching the ground with tiny decurved bills, some pattering with their feet knowing it would bring worms to the surface, others 'sounding' the mud, and all hungry after their vast journeying over lands and oceans beyond the knowledge of the fox.

They did not see Old Red move along the sea wall where mist-wet gorse brushed his coat, turning it dark. A family of stonechats watched him go, the black-headed adult male 'chacking' at him to tell him to leave his young well alone. They had been born here in a gorse-hidden nest, as their ancestors had before them, in the days when the gorse had been fodder for local cattle in winter and had fuelled the ovens of the cottagers and baked good bread.

Old Red saw humans at Horsey Island and he left the high bank to run through gorse and bramble to the sandy, rutted road near the White House. He hurried now in the daylight, trotting swiftly along the silent Toll Road until he came to the Toll Gate which he squeezed under, hearing the sounds of many swallows gathering above him on wires to discuss their impending journey to Africa for the winter. Now they had their young with them to follow them across oceans their kind had traversed since the breaking up of the land-masses many centuries before.

Old Red paused as a bright blue bird flashed before him to perch in the sallow growing by the Toll House dyke. Seeing the fox the kingfisher 'peeped' twice and was gone into the marshes.

Movement near the Toll House made him crouch and Old Red stiffened as a large dog fox backed away from a torn dustbin bag, turning towards him with a meaty bone in his jaws. The two foxes saw each other at the same moment and Old Red did not move as the other, a brindled fox the colours of a brown tabby cat came towards him carrying his prize.

The newcomer was five years old and had lived at Mainstone Woods near the village of Ashford until continuous tree-felling cost him his earth, forcing him to leave his birthplace to travel to these marshes three days before. On the first day the brindle fox had discovered a food source in the refuse bags at two cottages near Velator Crossing where a rat-torn bag had spilled its contents on to the roadside. The brown rat, with young to feed, had turned in anger on the fox only to die as the powerful animal had chomped her down where she stood and ate her, turning then to eat a number of sandwiches that had been thrown stale into the refuse. Thus are the ways of the opportunist hunter, with survival the stimulus.

Now he eyed Old Red closely, noting the well-muscled frame of the younger fox, the head-on stance and steady gaze that showed no wavering, and he moved on by the younger animal, jaws gripping the meat he had found, averting his gaze to look across the marshes, and he was gone along the track by a small vegetable garden. Old Red watched him go then turned away, moving swiftly now as he heard movements within the Toll House that told him people were about; the two foxes going their own ways with no room in their lives for friendship, only the life of a loner save for a mate, and for brief periods, their cubs.

The barn lair, hidden behind high hedge banks, was a welcome sight to Old Red as he slipped inside, a red shadow, to lie in his favourite spot, the earth within the building dug from soil piled high against one wall many years before.

Summer's End

• ◆ •

The hot summer passed swiftly, Old Red becoming a fully grown dog fox at ease with his wild world and the easy night hunting of the dunes and marshland of his birth. The days were shortening rapidly as hundreds of waders and numerous ducks and geese came to the estuary and marshes, their cries as wild as their native countryside as they wandered the mudflats or roosted in the grasslands when tides were high.

Fewer people wandered the area, only the regulars here at all times of the year, to 'get away from it all', some with their dogs, others botanising or birdwatching, all intent on their own pursuits and not bothering Old Red at all. Each day the sun rose and fell in a misty haze that spoke of the colder times to come, shining dully on the crimson of hawthorn berries, the scarlet of rosehips and old stalks of viper's bugloss and evening primrose long since flowerless, already touched with the first frosts of the new season.

On one such evening when the air was dampened by the blanket of mist over the estuary, Old Red ventured from the snug warmth of his lair, reluctant to move into the cold yet urged by a rumbling belly that told him it was time to find more food.

A flock of chaffinches flew low over the marsh fields to alight in the trees near Marstage, leaving again as thousands of starlings came from the east with a noisy whirring of wings to circle and perch, murmuring and chattering to each other. They perched all along the hedgerow, gleaming eyes studying the reed beds which would be their winter roosting area for yet another year. More came swarming in from the sea, their wing sounds like the very surf that beat upon the shore as they swept over the fox, causing him to duck his head.

He moved silently beneath a stone wall where the ground was churned into mud by cattle hooves. Here at a gateway he struck a mouse with one paw, killing it instantly and eating it where he stood. The house mouse, one of two-score living beneath the fallen roof and timbers of the old marsh barn adjoining the wall, had been eating a snail when Old Red struck it. Now the fox sniffed at the partly chewed snail, flicked it play-fully with a forepaw into the long grass by the gate and moved on past clumps of nettles which in June had been home to the eggs of red admiral butterflies arriving to breed from the Continent, then provided food for the larvae as they emerged in August.

Old Red paused to eat mushrooms growing from sheep-grazed grass, eating the tops of three before trotting on to where the green of the fields changed to sandy ground. He paused, drinking from an old cattle trough, lapping the ice-cold water which still held a few tadpoles hatched in the late spring and which had never matured to frogs as had those born in the warmer, nutrient-rich waters of the nearby dykes.

He moved on again into the Burrows, a stoat snarling at him as they met along the path that ran parallel with the boardwalk, the *Mustela* moving lithely away to its lair beneath the wooden slats. He was old, a stoat born four years before Old Red, in a hole begun by rabbits and lived in by little owls, and he would probably not live long beyond the coming winter.

Old Red knew the stoats well, knew their lairs and where the females had their nursery nests, just as the stoats knew of his earth; but other than by chance their paths rarely crossed.

Now he scattered soft sand as he ploughed down over the dune slopes at the boardwalk's end to reach the firmer terrain of the beach. He heard the piping cries of oystercatchers in the gathering darkness, seeing the white of their pied bodies amongst the rocks near the shore, but not the black-ness of their plumage that showed only in the day. He followed the sound seawards, the scent of the estuary filling his nostrils.   Reaching the tideline he splashed through the shallows of an ebbing tide, swinging away from three bobbing heads, which clanked as they touched, for the fox did not know about metallic floats nor did he wish to know. He paused as a large white head with black holes for eyes stared at him from the now starlit sands. But the object showed no life and Old Red moved on again passing the ram's skull which had floated and tumbled on waters running all the way from Exmoor to the Taw.

Old Red splashed through more pools amongst the sharp black rocks at the tide edge, reflected stars dancing upon the water with his passing. Curlews, oystercatchers and dunlin put up before him with shrill cries as he followed the waterline inland over Crow Neck from where he could see the lights of Appledore and Instow across the estuary. The mist had lifted from the river as Old Red made his way to the mouth of the Caen to follow the saltings to Velator.

He came upon a dead herring gull, crow-eaten and naught but head, feathers and feet and he left it for the morrow's burying beetles who would trundle their orange and black shining bodies to provide the long dead bird a funeral where it had fallen. Pushing through a hedge he ran along the silent road to Sandy Lane Farm where he disturbed two rats feeding on the remains of a mallard that had died of old age. They ran before him along a track, which led to a golf course, squealing with rage as they bounded onto a well-mown green where Old Red caught one of them by a hind leg, shaking and swinging the rat about until it was dead. He looked about him but the second rat had bolted into a rabbit hole, his rage now a fear as he heard his night-time companion utter its last squeal. Old Red ate it and ran on south-eastwards until he reached his home earth in the marsh barn as the first of the autumnal easterlies swept down the estuary of the Taw off Exmoor, a cold wind that had told the black grouse at Winn Brook, and the Hangley Cleave deer, that winter was on its way.

Of Winter Life on the Marshes

•◆•

The autumn had passed swiftly and uneventfully for the fox. He had lived well on rabbit, duck, blackberries, mushrooms and worms through a season that had been kind for much of its time as the days shortened and few people disturbed the peace of the place.

Now, on a night that spoke sharply of winter, an easterly wind blew cold across the marshes, moaning eerily through holes in the roof of the barn where Old Red lived. Moonlight filtering through the same holes glinted in two eyes that surveyed the outside world and noted every movement. The eyes were those of Old Red now nine months old and a fine fox with the experience and wisdom learned and earned rapidly in the wild.

The farmer who grazed his cattle on the marshes it was who had named him Old Red because of his redness of colour and the sharply contrasting greyness of muzzle that gave the fox the premature appearance of old age.

The farmer and the fox never bothered each other and Old Red had settled to a life on the marshes quite happily, learning early of the traps and snares sometimes concealed in hedgerows of the farmland where he hunted. Old Red had never taken a lamb for there was food enough in the area and thus it was the farmer had never regarded the fox with enmity. Often he had watched Old Red run homewards through the fields of sheep and cattle who barely stirred at his passing and were certainly far more troubled by the dogs from the nearby village.

The night was chilled by a frost for it was December, the warm spring and summer seeming long ago. Old Red's exhaled breaths each hung on the air for a moment and then were gone before his eyes as he watched the marsh, instinct telling him it was a good night to hunt. He moved silently from the old barn door which hung half in and half out of the building on broken rusty hinges. He started for a moment then relaxed as two barn owls flew over his head and out onto the marshes. They lived in the loft above the fox yet he had never become used to their silent appearances close over his head and he watched them fly white and ghostlike across the reed beds on downy wings, knowing that they too were hunting.

He watched them quartering the marshes for a while. All the world was silver and black, the shallow water of the nearby ponds reflecting the moonlight, sparkling where the icy breath of a winter breeze rippled the surface not quite frozen. Old Red left the barn, becoming part of the night, loping with head hung low and ears pricked to catch the slightest sound. Save for the usual murmur of waders on the foreshore, the night was quiet as he made his way along the edge of the reed bed, avoiding the pools where ice was forming on the shallowest for he had learned that the crackling of breaking ice warned of his coming. On he moved deeper into the marshes, swinging wide of an area where he had once sunk up to his chin and had known real fear. Now he was amongst alder and sallow on drier ground forming an island of solid land with shrub and tree cover.

Old Red sniffed for a moment at the spraints of otter on a grassy hummock then moved without sound between the trees to reach his favourite hunting area.

Standing starkly black against the background of dead reeds and yellow flag was the derelict hulk of an old barge, a relic of bygone days when this part of the meandering marsh was the River Caen now flowing some quarter of a mile away, moved to its present course by the work of Irish and Dutch navvies a century and a half ago, to reclaim the land for grazing cattle and sheep. The ancient barge had been left to rot on the river bank and now lay hidden by trees, the home of many rats, woodlice and sometimes passing otters.

Old Red crept forward with what could only be called a grin on his handsome face then suddenly he tensed and dropped quickly to the ground. Low over the reeds came the ghostly shape of a barn owl whilst in the distance its mate screeched, the sound carrying far into the night. The owls were hunting together now, their keen eyesight and extraordinary hearing much more acute than even Old Red's.

Rats moved on rotten boards, the scrabbling sound reflected along the white disc of the nearest owl's face, carrying to its ears. Old Red watched it drop with outstretched legs and sharp talons to rise again in one flowing movement, a rat hanging limply. All happened at once! The second owl appeared from nowhere and rats were all about the fox who snapped and shook without thinking. He threw three to one side dead in as many seconds as the remainder disappeared beneath the barge screaming and squealing. Picking up the largest, Old Red trotted off after the two laden owls already nearing the barn and was soon feeding contentedly on the warm straw and sacking in his corner of the old building. In the loft two white owls roosted, leaning on each other in peaceful slumber.

Of Collie Dogs and Ducks

•◆•

On a cold grey morning when high winds tossed dead leaves into Old Red's hideout, he ventured out on to the marshes which lay drably green and brown under weak winter sunlight that filtered through the cloud cover. A mistle thrush called from the topmost branches of a swaying alder tree, boldly facing into the wind, letting the rushing air snatch its song and carry it to all the marsh inhabitants. A grey heron stood hunched with its back to the wind, surveying the ponds where dead reedmace leaves barely reflected on the wind-scuffed surface of the icy water. Two little grebes swam from the reeds, reaching the centre of the pool to up-end and dive beneath as Old Red appeared at the water-side. A wisp of snipe flew in over the dead elm trees still bordering the Royal Marine Station at Chivenor, to spread out along the sedge-strewn marsh fields; the fox, nosing along the water's edge, put up a moorhen which squawked loudly, exploding from the reeds fringing the water. It ran rapidly over the surface with splashing feet and flapping wings to drop into the reeds on the far bank.

A score of beef cattle appeared over the high bank bordering reclaimed marshland. Seeing Old Red they stood around him in a tight circle, snorting and lowering their heads as they eyed him curiously. Old Red walked towards the animal immediately in his way, whereupon it lost its nerve and turned to bolt across the marsh field, its hooves throwing up great clods of earth as it ran, followed suddenly by the others. Along the bank where stood a stone barn by the Caen river, a lone birdwatcher caught sight of the running cattle and, focussing his binoculars, saw that they were followed by a trotting fox, an observation carefully written into his notebook; 'fox herding cattle' was an amusing aspect of animal behaviour whatever the real cause. The cattle swerved as one, galloping across the open marshland away from the reed beds, putting to flight a cloud of birds which wheeled and soared as they sorted swiftly into species; the broad wings of hundreds of lapwing showed black then white as they flew high over the wetland, while a mass of golden plovers swept swiftly by them in a tight flock heading for the estuary mudflats. Old Red had now reached the deep bend in the ponds where they curled back to the alder island and beyond to dense reed beds and a sewage farm. Here he chased after a water rail stalking sedately with its high-stepping gait amongst the waterside vegetation. The slender bird flew up in front of the fox's face and with trailing legs fluttered from view as Old Red halted, frustrated by its easy escape. He walked on, the soft ground yielding beneath his paws, showing the tracks of his passing. Near a natural stone wall built at right-angles across the trackway he trotted up on to the bank, leaping a stile to find a large brown-winged bird quartering the open grassland before him, swerving from side to side and canting its wings, its flight buoyant and easy as it searched for mouse, vole or small birds for its prey. The female hen harrier swung about in flight, seeing the fox on the river bank. Flapping her long wings she flew over him to begin diligently quartering the marshes again, her ringtail clearly showing as she flew.

The fox had seen her many times, she and her kind wintering in the Westcountry's wilder places, sometimes taking starlings, coot and even teal from the marshes. He returned to his own task of finding food and upon reaching the road to the Burrows he ran swiftly along it, following the dyke until he came to farm buildings at the roadside and could see amongst the sedges and rushes, the heads of several ducks showing. He ran at these, passing the farm entrance where he was seen by a small black and white collie, which immediately howled and gave chase. Old Red increased his speed as he heard the howling, dashing amongst the ducks to catch a Muscovy by the neck, both fox and bird falling into the dyke as the collie rushed barking and snarling frenziedly in its eagerness to do battle with the fox.

Fortunately for Old Red, the dog's jaws closed on the duck he was holding, dragging, to his side, and as they fell into the water he released it, swimming for the opposite bank with powerful strokes. He hauled himself from the cold water, shaking himself as dry as he could, turning to see the collie barking madly but unwilling to give chase across the dyke. Old Red shook himself again, moving on towards the toll road

which he followed until he came to another reed-fringed pool sheltered by a sea wall with gorse bushes along one side of it.

A small flock of teal put up at his approach, becoming specks in the grey sky as they sped towards Isley Marshes on the other side of the estuary. Old Red nosed around the garden of the White House, out on to Crowe Beach where he followed the shoreline, ringed plover and a few sanderling scattering before him like silvery leaves. The fox ate the flesh of a half grapefruit cast on the shore by the tide, then found a dead herring gull which he left for it was oil-covered and stank. He trotted in the shallows along the beach to where three cormorants stood, wings held wide, skirting around them to dash amongst a flock of gulls for the fun of it as they flew about his head screaming defiance at this insult. On he ran, soon losing them as he loped easily inland towards the dunes which spread parallel with the sea. Finding a break in the dunes he trotted through marram and dead sea holly clumps, sending up a flock of goldfinches from where they fed on the seed-heads of thistles, running again by Doughnut Pond and the dunes of his early days. He skirted this pool, putting up a snipe, which flew with a 'squaaark' over the nearest dune, and ran on tongue lolling to where a large expanse of wet slack stretched before him to even higher dunes.

Old Red followed the route of vehicle tracks here, the going easier, drinking from where rainwater lay in them, arriving at 'J' lane where several rabbits scattered into holes and dense brambles. He spent some time exploring these, sniffing at each entrance hole. Poking his head into bramble clumps but finding no prey, he loped on; crossing the rutted track that served as a road, leaping the ditches dug to prevent vehicles being driven into the dunes by unthinking motorists, and making his way across the Velator dykes once again.

Two boys were by the side of the dyke as Old Red leapt the hedge bank into the field where he trotted under cover of the hawthorn hedge in order to pass them. As he approached the gateway leading into the field the boys clambered over having finished their play at the waterside. Old Red paused, confused, then quickly leapt back through a gap in the hedge to the roadway. No one was about and the boys, intent on their game of exploring had not seen him. He followed the dyke along the grass verge, coming upon the carcass of the Muscovy duck he had taken earlier, lying on the grass. It had been pulled from the water earlier by one of the youngsters who were now playing in the field having soon lost interest and turned to other matters.

Old Red glanced about him. He bit deeply into the duck, lifting the heavy bird to trot along the marsh road with his prize. Once past the farm he dropped the bird, readjusting his grip and trotting on again to his marshland home, occasionally resting for brief moments then resuming his way until eventually he was once again back at the old building. He ate well from the duck, saving much of the bird, which would stay him yet another day or two.

Of Wildfowlers And WildFowl

◆

The days of winter passed uneventfully enough for the occupants of the old barn. One or two birdwatchers came regularly to the marshes and quietly huddled in the reed beds, watching the wintering birds and making notes of teal, gadwall, water rail and bearded reedlings, even a bittern brought by harder weather elsewhere. Old Red occasionally saw them prowling across the countryside or hiding behind hedge banks, as grey herons stalked the pond edges hunting frogs and other food. The birdwatchers never bothered the fox or entered his lair; seemed a harmless lot.

Memories of his tragic early days filtered mistily back into his mind only when wildfowlers were present. They would enter the reed beds to spread out, shooting various duck and snipe which they put up. Twice during leaner days the fox had taken advantage of this situation, the first time purely by chance, the second learned from experience of the first.

Old Red had been returning to the barn shortly after dawn one morning when voices caused him to lie low, his long nose resting between red campions that had bloomed late, refusing to bow to the winter. Suddenly ducks were flying all around him and the sound and shockwaves of explosions shook his ears and body. As unexpected as the sounds of the shots, a drake mallard fell in front of the fox so instinctively he seized it, bolting into the reeds and soon lying with his prize in the old building.

A puzzled farmer, gun under his arm, searched with his spaniels for the bird he had seen crash into the reeds, but in vain.

Old Red's second mallard was taken on the run from the little island amongst the reeds only a few days later. At neither time was the fox sighted.

That night, around a log fire at the nearby inn, the story of the missing ducks passed to and fro across the flickering fireplace.

'Well, Harold, I saw'n go down as plain's a pikestaff but 'ee must have winged it and it crawled off into the reeds,' said one wildfowler from behind his pint of best bitter.

'Seems darn funny to me,' said Harold, an expert shot with a 12-bore. 'That's two mallard 'ave gone down now and disappeared, Jack. Strikes me they'm breeding a tougher species of duck. It's all this evolution you knows.'

Jack quaffed deeply at his ale. 'Aye perhaps you'm right, Harold,' he said settling back in his chair, his mind already on other things.

Two miles away Old Red slept deeply. As he breathed out, little mallard feathers scattered from his nostrils in the breeze he made.

Of a Storm and a Move

•◆•

Much of the winter had passed by, slowly and coldly said many people, but Old Red had hunted when the weather permitted and slept away many of the hours of cold and rain in his lair.

April had arrived almost unnoticed, for the cold had kept the marshes and burrows much the same day after day. These were not the places of celandines proclaiming the coming of springtime, the main Burrows flora more obvious beyond the merry month of May. Just a few people continued to visit the marshes, the farmers who checked their stock and the fences, and one who was always seen about the dykes with a JCB vehicle cleaning out the vegetation and silt to keep the water sweet-running.

But the official springtime had arrived at March end, passing without much ado. Men, women and children had tensed themselves to cope with April 1st and the April Fool's Day fun that still persists in friendly country districts. But this year it rained and somehow dampened the spirits of the fun-seekers, other than a tiny few cajoled out by a leading local naturalist, whose reputation suggested they should not miss such a sighting, to see 'rare rose-coloured swans'. And so they tramped miles in the pouring rain to find only white mute swans, later to be told, 'well, you have seen white roses haven't you?!' Such are the moments that fill people's lives.

That night, as the cold winter hours passed by and wildfowlers slept snugly in their beds, a stillness fell upon the marshes. Then, at about three in the morning, came the first crashes and deep rumblings of thunder from out at sea. Somewhere in the Westcountry a weather forecaster turned over in his bed and smiled to himself. Got that one right, he thought, and went back to sleep.

With the first lightning and rolls of thunder, rain fell over the whole area, torrential rain, huge gusts of wind driving it in from the sea and up the estuary to turn the land into a soaking mess of mud and streaming water. Old Red kept waking and falling fitfully asleep again even though he was well fed and warm. Day came and brought no let-up in the weather, the fox just gazing into the greyness at the horizontally sweeping rain that reduced his world to but a few yards from his lair. He idly watched the one or two birds which sought shelter in the barn. Awed by the storm, a blackbird, wren, two grey wagtails and a meadow pipit perched on beams around the inside of the building, twittering softly at every creaking of boards and slamming of broken window frames. Higher in the building the two barn owls perched together eyes half-closed. Great gusts of wind howled at over one hundred miles an hour as raging seas cut the land all along the coast. Boats broke their moorings on the Caen, sweeping downstream with swirling tree debris, and carried on to the estuary, some already filling with water and keeling over on their sides as they went.

Several Brent geese of the dark-bellied race appeared on the Taw, with them a score of white-fronts, as intrepid birdwatchers braved a soaking to get a closer look at such rarities in the area.

Darkness fell early, no moon showing through the turmoil of storm clouds. It was just after sunset, and whilst Old Red was dozing, that a roaring gust of wind hit the barn, such a gust as all the others put together it seemed. The fox was immediately wide-awake, running into the rain and wind to the sound of roaring and the crashing of timbers. The instinctive action saved his life for where he had lain moments before there now lay the massive rotting timbers and beams of the barn roof.

Old Red stopped running as the roaring sound ceased. Turning to look back at the building that had been his home for almost a year, his coat clinging wetly to his lean frame, he could see two barn owls buffeted by less powerful gusts as they flew above the damaged building, tossed as white corks on an invisible sea. Somehow Old Red knew there was no returning home to the barn. The instinct of wild creatures, so far beyond our own comprehension, is such that it seems born of great wisdom.

Old Red turned away. He trotted along the towpath by the Caen in which whole trees now floated towards the estuary, glancing off the remaining boats and each other as they were swept on by a flood that could turn the very tide. He passed two small cottages and some hen coops before coming to the disused railway level crossing at Velator. Here he glanced to left and right, deciding to follow the walk route that stretched in a straight line before him towards the ancient market town of Barnstaple. He followed the track of the old railway at a fast trot in pouring rain, three miles at that pace finding him cold, soaked and foot-sore close to the town. Old Red was so weary he did not notice the many lapwing sheltering under gorse along the route as he doggedly kept going, though he knew not where, head low on aching shoulders, eyes straining into the dark rain-filled night.

The first light of dawn saw him turn down the embankment of the Bradiford Water to follow the flooded stream to a main road which he crossed, then slipped under a gateway leading up over a sloping field where a stone folly topped the ridge between pine trees. Old Red turned right along a narrow lane called Poleshill where tall, mature trees swayed in the now quieting winds, the grey morning light showing a landscape of debris and mud.

Crossing a minor road, the fox splashed along Halls Mill Lane where great pools of water rendered the terrain stream-like. A dog barked as he passed Anchor Mills but Old Red paid it no heed. Tired and hungry he squeezed beneath a gate with a stile to cross three more fields to where a rough wire fence prevented cattle from entering an old wood on the hillside. He ran by an ancient, gnarled beech tree, past a roaring weir and into a disused quarry overgrown with bramble and hawthorn. Here Old Red quickly hid himself beneath a rock overhang, falling fast asleep, exhausted by the night's events.

Of a New Home

◦•◦

Old Red awoke as the last rays of the setting sun appeared to set fire to the ancient beech tree at the entrance to the wood, as it had done for nigh on five hundred years. For a few moments the tree was lit by an orange glow and then turned to black silhouette, as a log left in a dying fire. Somewhere a blackbird 'pink-pinked' to the disappearing day and then was quiet. The dog fox rose and stretched, testing his cramped muscles and shaking his coat free of the last vestiges of dampness. He had slept for two whole days in his new-found sanctuary and was warm but hungry, weakened by the events of the recent stormy night. He had no knowledge of the days just gone by; that the storm had quickly abated, that the sun had warmed the valley, quickening the spring growth of buds and flowers on trees and shrubs in the hedge banks and wood. It had warmed him even as he slept, healing him with his resting.

Old Red stealthily moved out of the quarry, standing for a moment bathed in silvery moonlight at the woodland edge, realising suddenly that he was in new territory. He did not really know where he was or where to go.

The scene before him was of a large water meadow bounded by high hedgerows on three sides, with wide open grassland where alder and willow grew tall along a line of ancient mill leat. Beside him the water of the leat flowed slowly beneath dense vegetation. To his left sounded the roar of a weir where it flowed black and glistening to white water foam and then to the stream winding away in the moonlight. Old Red followed the leat to where a gap showed a trackway into the mass of Himalayan balsam by the water. Here he trotted across an old wooden plank bridge, silently making his way along the hedgerow to where the leat met the main stream again. He followed the stream for a while, coming to a fallen oak spanning the waterway, and crossed over to enter a sloping field under cover of more willow and alder trees. In the distance a farm dog barked, the sound carrying far across the valley as Old Red, unheeding, made his way to the top of a bank which overlooked a meadow. There in the field in the moonlight were several rabbits, their scent blown to the fox, making his mouth hang open and watering. Two rabbits were quite close by him chomping the lush grass, while two more chased in a slow circle nearby, these dividing a further group of seven all feeding quietly.

Old Red wasted not a second, dashing headlong at the nearest, a buck, the undisputed leader of this colony, who promptly somersaulted with fright causing the snapping jaws of the fox to miss him completely. The fox did not pause but ran directly at the second rabbit, a plump doe who cried a blood-curdling scream and died abruptly. Old Red stood with his prey held firmly and looked about him. Not a rabbit was in sight, nor was there a sound, as he loped steadily back across the stream with his prize. Hidden in the bramble brake along the edge of the field, the other rabbits crouched, already getting over the shock of the sudden arrival of the predator in their midst. Soon they would be feeding again with only that thought in their minds.

And so Old Red learned quickly of the immense richness of wildlife in the wooded valley where springtime promised much. He made his way jauntily back towards the woods by a more circuitous route than that by which he had come and it was thus that he arrived at the place he was to choose as his home for some time to come.

High in the woods, where the years had worn away high banks, an old tree had fallen to a storm. Here behind torn roots was a natural cavern, dry and leaf-filled into which the weary but contented fox crept with his rabbit prey. Old Red fed well that night, leaving meat for the next day, and was soon asleep in his shelter.

Thus it was that a storm had rendered the fox homeless but two days previously whilst, many years before, another had created his newly found lair.

Spring Days

•◆•

An early April morning found Old Red awaking to the sound of a dawn chorus which now included willow warbler and chiffchaff songs, several of the summer migrant species having arrived in their breeding areas. The sweet descending trill of a willow warbler sounded close over his head as he gazed out at his new-found home. The fox had been working for two days on enlarging his lair, making a second exit or entrance hole in the earth bank at the back, which lead into an open field. Not happy with the one original entrance the fox had spent several hours improving his home, digging powerfully with his strong forepaws, and throwing the earth out behind him with his hind legs.

On this first day of the singing of willow warblers, Old Red had finally broken through into dense brambles and bracken at the side of the hedge bank where it joined the wood edge. The last fall of soil slid into the field, the earth and stones pushing aside the ferns growing there and allowing the fox a clear view over the countryside.

Away to one side lay Blakewell Mill where a few farm buildings blended into the country scene. Here the woods lay green and peaceful below fields where sheep and cattle spread out grazing contentedly, proclaiming fine weather. Old Red rested from his labours, watching a tractor working the field adjoining the woods where he now lived. He crouched low whenever the vehicle passed close, watching the driver puffing away at his pipe, high up in his little cabin. Several gulls followed the vehicle, screaming and wailing as they watched for any morsel thrown up by the dragging of the ground.

A buzzard soared high over the trees, switch-backing in display flight to his mate, then gliding swiftly down above the steep hillside on half-closed wings, its piercing, mewing cry sounding even above the noise of the tractor's engine as the hawk flew into the treetops close to their nest-site of many years.

Old Red dozed, his earth now suiting him, his eyes occasionally opening to watch the day. A pair of long-tailed tits searched for feathers to complete the lining of their nest in the brambles nearby, hidden by its camouflage of mosses, lichens and spiders'-web silk. The busy birds would collect a thousand or more tiny feathers to provide warmth for their forthcoming eggs and young in this one nest.

In trees across the field raucous cries issued as a rook took a stick from another rook's nest and carefully laid it on its own. It was smallish rookery of seven nests made in three trees standing close together above a farm lane.

A cuckoo called from an oak branch further along the hedgerow as smaller birds became agitated at its presence, flying to harass it away from their nest sites in various stages of construction or use. The cuckoo called again, more to proclaim his arrival in the area than to any mate, as the females had not yet arrived to begin their own task of laying in the nests of other species.

In a garden opposite the woods at Westaway an elderly woman noted the date of the first cuckoo of the year in her diary, then went indoors to drop a line to the local newspaper to report the fact.

The cuckoo, unaware of his fame, left his perch to fly hedge-hopping along the valley towards Bradiford village, passing low over cattle and sheep, and a farmer repairing a wire fence.

The drone of the tractor engine ceased. The man repairing the fence stood back mopping his brow, a glance at the position of the sun telling him it was time for lunch, and he wended his way eagerly homeward towards the whitewashed cottage close by the farmhouse.

In the field above the woods the tractor and drag stood quietly, the driver sitting munching his sandwiches, content with a good morning's work in kind weather. His keen eyes sought out the fox crouching in its earth and he grinned to himself as he ate. Each time he had passed around the field he had cast his eye along the hedge bank, seeing the fox's head drop from sight behind the bramble brake. Cheese mingled with the tang of pickled onions tasted fine in the open air; the farmer was happy with his lot, the countryside his life, as it had been his father's and grandfather's before.

He had no quarrel with Old Red. Some farmers shot foxes, some left them to the Hunt, some to their own devices. He was of the latter per-suausion, and if the fox did not bother his livestock, he would not bother it. Just a day or two previously he had watched Old Red sitting in the early morning sunshine as four pheasants fed along the hedgerow bottom close by, not such a rare sight but one to set anyone thinking.

He poured strong tea from his flask, settling back to enjoy the sunshine and birdsong where once, as a boy, he had learned with his father the ways of wild creatures and the changing seasons.

Old Red curled himself into his sleeping position, his instincts telling him he was safe here in his new home, and dozing, fell asleep.

Later that same afternoon the fox awoke and stared about him. The tractor had gone and before him lay the empty field. Rooks strutted about it now, the gulls gone to the estuary and its tidal river, a glimpse of which was just visible from the hilltop hedge bank above the woods.

The early evening chorus of birdsong told of blackbirds, robins, and warblers, the valley ringing with many melodies, each so different from the other, yet blending into a symphony of delightful sound.

Old Red arose, trotting down over the field beside the woods to the stream which he reached by crossing another pasture field, finding a spot where the water ran slow and clear.

A brown trout darted away as Old Red's nose broke the surface of the water. As he drank he could see the many-coloured stones at the bottom of the stream and several minnows swam across his vision into the deep green world of waterweeds. Above him on a branch, close to the ivy-covered trunk of a leaning oak, a tawny owl perched on its favourite daytime roost, below which lay a number of pellets, the regurgitated remains of past meals of voles, mice and other creatures encapsulated within their own fur.

The fox turned from the stream refreshed, sniffing at the dark-grey pellets.

Remembering those dropped by the barn owls of his former marshland home, then moving on, he crossed a shallow pool formed by a trickling stream running down along a narrow overgrown lane, the water hidden beneath lushly growing ferns for much of its length. Above the sunken route a path had been worn by the passage of many feet over many years, the fox following this by wild garlic whose pure white flowers would clearly show the way on dark nights. He reached a stile built across the top of the lane, sniffing at a plank seat and drawing back with a snarl at the scent of humans who had sat there earlier in the day.

Movement in the long grass caught his keen eyes and he stiffened into stillness, his long ears pointed, alert, his liquid gold eyes searching for the cause of movement. Moments passed, then the vegetation parted as a long sinewy shape emerged, darkly furred and lithe, followed by another, the two moving snarling to one side as they saw Old Red confronting them.

The fox watched the two lope into the dense undergrowth beneath a group of beech trees, seeing them disappear towards the farm he knew was in the distance. He had seen such creatures before, on the marshes of his early days, and knew they killed waterfowl and fish for he had watched them do so at idle times. They were mink of the *Mustela* family, cousins of the stoats, weasels, otters and badgers. Their ancestors had been imported to fur farms to provide pelts for humans to wear and profit from. Now they were running wild and breeding, feral mink descended from several which had escaped or been released from the farms that had sought to gain from them on Dartmoor, their spread across the Westcountry rapid.

The first mink of the two, a female, had been born here in the valley, a mile upstream, in the hollow of a huge ash tree that had seen the comings and goings of many wild creatures. She had fled her home at an early age when her mother had grown tired of parental duties and had snarled and spat at her family of three swiftly growing youngsters. They had dispersed into the countryside to fend for themselves, as is the way of the wild, and now at mating age she had met her companion, an adult male, under Bradiford Bridge but a week before. He, wandering the country-side to find a mate had entered the Bradiford Water at its confluence with the great Taw river, having swum it from Fremington Creek where he had been born.

Old Red watched for signs of further movement but the mink had moved on. Under the fence at the top of the lane he went, following a sheep track that ran along the steeply sloping field. A thick bramble hedge led to a gateway where Old Red prowled about in scrub oak and hazel, then with the sun still warm on his back, he left the thicket to trot along a dip in the ground beside the hedgerow. Primroses and violets made splashes of bright colour whilst the golden yellow of coltsfoot flowers grew without leaves here and there in cheerful clumps along the clay bank.

A mistle thrush scolded the fox as he passed too close to where the bird's mate was sitting on eggs, and then a crow dived at his head for the sheer pleasure of doing so, craawing loudly as it shot over his head, as if laughing to see the fox scamper for cover below it. The crow dived again, lower, losing a tail feather as Old Red snarled and leapt agilely at it, surprising the usually wily bird who craaawed again, this time with alarm, and promptly flew over the hedge and was gone.

The fox moved lithely up the steep rise and, seeing the farm and outbuildings before him, detoured below them and a narrow access road. This ran below newer houses and a renovated mill that had once been an ice cream factory and was now a dwelling house. He crossed more fields, coming almost to Blakewell and stood in the shade of a patch of gorse to get his bearings. A long shadow moved beside an open gate leading on to a narrow road and Old Red flung himself around, whirling into the cover of the gorse and bolting as some sixth sense screamed danger into his mind.

Where he had been standing the grass and earth flew up, the ground peppered with 12-bore shot as, cursing, the farmer who owned the land let go with the second barrel, missing the fox by yards as it vanished over the hedge bank.

The farmer grinned to himself as he recalled how the fox had all but somersaulted as its instincts had warned it of danger. This one was new to the area and a real cunning one at that, he told himself.

Two fields away and still running fast Old Red, neared the safety of the woods at a gallop. Recognising the terrain he slowed to a trot, heading for his earth, as one of the mink he had seen earlier moved out of its tree-hole den in a hollow oak, then shot back in again in fright at the sight of the fox running straight towards it along the bank of the stream.

Minutes later, the first female blackcap to arrive for the summer perched on a branch a few feet above the secluded lair of Old Red. They both rested from their flights, the bird tired after flying thousands of miles from its tropical wintering haunts, the fox from its headlong dash of a mile across the countryside.

Of Otters, Cats and Grey Fleck

•→•

Owl light, the dimmity of Westcountry folk, was on the meadows; with it came the harsh cry of a grey heron flapping its lone way home to the heronry at Arlington where it lived for the spring months with sixty more of its kind in an ancient heronry above a lake.

The heron's harsh call echoed across the open valley below, and Old Red glanced up as the great grey bird slowly flapped along the route of the stream, the fox's long white chin and throat gleaming in the fading light as he stared skywards.

Old Red was standing by Dead Man's Pool where a few moments earlier he had seen movement before the heron had called to the setting sun. Here at Dead Man's Pool grew three alder trees, a large ash and two oaks, one of which leaned out over the deep water as if staring down into its cool depths, two spreading branches like arms reaching for the fish that often swam there. The fresh water, sweeping down from the rain-soaked hills of Exmoor's fringe country, slowed here, swirling the grasses and leaves torn from stream banks in a sweeping circle; plunging on beneath Shearford Bridge in a torrent of ochre-coloured water carrying the sediment from the hills beyond.

A fir cone from the trees by Playford Mill bobbed about the pool and under the roots of the leaning oak, knocking against them with faint tapping sounds as it went, watched by dark liquid eyes set in a whiskered face as wise as time itself. Here within the dark cavern formed by roots of the old oak, lay Lutra, a three-year-old dog otter born in a holt barely a mile away and now back in his home area after two months spent around the estuary of the Taw and Torridge rivers.

The otter was sleek and fit, the living good in this countryside where his ancestors had lived for hundreds of years before man had taken the land and farmed it. Now he lay still and content after feeding on small brown trout taken beneath Bradiford Bridge the night before. He had swum away from the bridge and under two more before finding the old holt used by otters for many a year. Lutra had watched Old Red loping

•51•

through the high grasses towards the stream bank where hours before he had marked territory with his spraints at the bend in the stream adjoining the bridge's single arch. He, too, heard the cry of the heron and watched its faint reflection fly upstream along the surface of the water. Soon it was lost as the bird wheeled above white water rushing over large stones laid to help walkers over this ancient footpath route.

The last light of day slipped into the murky greyness of a swiftening night as the handsome face of Old Red peered briefly into the otter's hiding place and moved away. Lutra heard the fox sniffing about the oak roots but he moved not, for the fox was no enemy, the otter fearing only man and his dogs. He did not know that here on this waterway he was free, for the waterway was one of many otter havens in the vicinity agreed by the farming landowners who no longer hunted otters.

Old Red peered again into the darkness beyond the tree roots. He knew the otter was there and he pricked his ears forward, hearing no sound save that of the water curling darkly about the tree roots.

He moved on downstream passing alder and elder, trotting beneath hawthorn now in full blossom, his feet moving on cool primroses and the leaves of bluebells, leaving his footprints in the mud where two fields joined linked by an old hedgerow and ditch. At the footbridge spanning the water between the mill field and Manning's Pit, he paused to cross and then, snarling, leapt away as his keen eyes saw a looming shape upon the bridge. The shape did not move and Old Red's lips curled back over sharp fangs as he loped away towards Anchor Mills where he slipped under a stile fence momentarily bathed in the light cast by a lantern suspended over the mill door.

From the footbridge a man watched the fox run across the field and into Halls Mill Lane, his own keen eyes watching the glow of the red coat until the fox was lost in the darkness beyond. The man had been standing for over an hour watching and listening for night wildlife, enjoying the peace of the place, knowing an otter was in the vicinity for he had searched for and found its spraints earlier in the day. The fox's sudden and silent arrival was not unusual to the naturalist for he, too, was a silent loner, not so unlike the foxes and otters in his own way, knowing well the countryside and the many stories told by its tracks and signs. Now he leaned on the bridge rail and watched on, content with wild company and knowing some night soon the otter also might pass his way in full view.

A tawny owl hooted from the trees near Hume's Farm at the end of the lane, its call carrying to the naturalist's ears and to those of Old Red nearing the road at the end of the lane. Every sense alert, he crouched low against a stone wall as a beam of light swept along the road, illuminating the hedgerow and trees in sharp detail as a car passed on its way to the town nearby. Old Red crossed the road in the sudden blackness left by the passing vehicle lights, trotting northwards to Upcott where he left the road to follow a driveway to a large white house overlooking the estuary of the Taw. Scenting food he soon located a row of bins beside the house and sniffing excitedly he stood on hind legs, pulling the first bin over and spilling its contents across the drive. Old Red ate three meat sandwiches and the remains of a cooked chicken, his jaws chomping with relish at his find.

Suddenly a spitting fury landed on his back. Old Red spun round, snapping in fear and anger as a huge white tom cat sank claws and teeth into the lean muscles of his flanks. Rolling and snapping, spitting and yowling, the two antagonists fell amongst the refuse, the fall dislodging the cat from Old Red's body, whereupon the fox promptly bolted across lawn and flowerbeds to find open country beyond a wire fence surrounding the private land. The white cat, back arched and still spitting, stared after the fox with his one blue and one green eye flashing hatred at this intruder in his domain; but the fox was gone, running fast across fields to where the village of Ashford showed its lights, his scratches and pride smarting at the sudden encounter.

He ran along a damp lane where grew lords and ladies and early purple orchids in profusion and into a goyal where he stopped to rest, panting a little but no longer hungry after his sandwich and chicken meal.

Suddenly he tensed, listening with head on one side as whimpering sounds came from the bushes bordered by white-flowered stems of cow parsley. A light breeze blew the scent of fox to him and Old Red stepped towards the sounds calling a soft, low whining to the unseen fox. The sound was immediately returned. Old Red moved forward as a rising moon tipped its pale light into the hollow, turning the cow parsley pure white against the blackness and illuminating the spot where lay Grey Fleck the vixen.

As Old Red moved forward the vixen tried to raise herself, whimpering to him, but fell back panting on to the soft bracken where for four days she had lain thus, her only food earthworms taken half-heartedly from about her aching head. Old Red whined to her, licking her face and ears, telling the vixen he was there. He nuzzled her hot body, feeling the matted pelt of a fox too sick to care for itself, the skin already loose on the lean frame.

Grey Fleck was in her second spring and had been born with two sisters and a brother to One Ear the vixen who had hunted Ashford and Heanton villages for a number of years with another vixen; the two lived as a family group, pooling their litters in the manner of some foxes. Grey Fleck had become ill during the late winter months, finding difficulty in hunting, becoming weaker and more listless with the arrival of spring. She was sick with pollution poisoning, toxic chemicals absorbed into her system with the intake of her food and now she lay gasping beside Old Red, her nose hot and stomach pained with hunger. The dog fox's tongue licked her face. She closed her eyes, thankful for the touch of a friend, laying her head back and heaving a sigh as if to say, 'I would hunt with you but I cannot.'

Old Red stepped back and gazed about him. The moonlit landscape showed the river as a silver ribbon beyond the trees. He left the vixen where she lay, moving across a field and trotting through a derelict tarmac-covered compound, then beneath trees where a female buzzard lay sleeping on her nest with four eggs. Now he was in an area of concrete paths, sheds and stacked fencing where trees and many plants stood in neat rows awaiting sale to gardeners all over the region. He passed buildings, moving on to lawns watched by the stony eyes of many garden gnomes awaiting new homes. On the south side of a low hedge he came upon a sleeping grey partridge, which died under the first snap of his jaws.

Old Red bit again, his jaws watering at his capture and ran back the way he had come with his prize gripped firmly. Nearing the goyal he slowed, listening, hearing again the whimper of Grey Fleck. He trotted proudly to her, dropping the fresh partridge by her raised head. She licked the plump bird, feeling Old Red's own tongue upon her face, her heart warming to him despite her weakness.

Old Red watched her nose at the partridge and begin to take feathers from its breast. Turning, he moved away up out of the goyal and along the orchard-hidden lane towards his home, his thoughts now directed towards his own hunting.

Minutes later, passing under the stile fence at Anchor Mills, he slowed by the footbridge but the human had gone. At a ditch between the mill fields he glimpsed a shining object before him close to the edge of the stream, finding it was a salmon partly eaten by Lutra and left on the bank. The otter was fast asleep in his oak-tree holt and Old Red ate ravenously from the succulent fish which had only recently penetrated the Bradiford Water off the Taw on its spring migration to its spawning redds.

The fox ate where he stood, then belly filled, he drank from the stream and moved on to his earth above the moonlit woods.

Of a Farmyard in Spring

•◆•

A May evening full of birdsong and the hum of bees found Old Red sitting on the bank of the stream above the weir, sunlight filtering through the oak and ash leaf canopy, turning his coat red and gold. Above the weir pool where the water slowed before dashing over in a white torrent, hoverflies danced in the sunbeams; around them a swarm of smaller flies of a species of *Hilera* also danced, a mating swarm of predatory insects, themselves hunting midges.

A herd of black and white Friesian cows moved into the meadow from the farm track at Westaway, causing a great cloud of long-legged crane-flies disturbed by their passing, to rise, fly low over the grass then settle again. Old Red decided all was well in the valley and woods. Rising he trotted off along the lower path in the direction of Blakewell. Above him the wooded slope was a mass of bluebells, drifts of blue as if the sky had lain to rest from the day amidst the rich springtime greenery of their own leaves beneath the freshly leaved oaks and beeches.

The warm golden light of a spring evening glowed richly on Old Red's coat as he paused to drink from the stream then move on into the deeper countryside of Muddiford and Plaistow.

At a converted mill he swung wide from where a few people sat eating cream teas on the lawn. No one saw him pass by under the shrubs at the end of the garden where old pig houses told of bygone farming days, and once well-used farm machinery had been cleaned and painted black as items of interest for tourists to stare at.

Old Red splashed across a stream that flows from Muddiford village, disturbing a swarm of eels swimming upstream after a three-year life at sea. The eels scattered beneath the fox's splashing feet then regrouped to swirl onwards as one. All winter the eels had fed around the coast as elvers and were now penetrating inland, yellow-coloured and voracious, to feed on crustacea, worms and frogs during their summer stay. The eels swirled around Old Red's legs once more as he trotted amongst them, cooling his feet, and then turned their heads into the current to continue on their way.

A barn owl flew from its perch in a linhay, screeching over Old Red's head as he loped down over a field, with distant memories of two barn owls doing much the same during his time at Braunton marshes. The fox followed a line of newly planted chestnut trees as the white owl passed low over his head, causing him to duck. The bird vanished along a ride between planted forestry trees where it often found the voles it loved to eat, Old Red following the pale ghost-like bird into the darkness. Eventually he came to a small field with farm outbuildings grouped about a straw-strewn yard, the home of the barn owls being in the hay bales of one of the buildings.

In the evening light once more, Old Red was crossing the yard when suddenly two Canada geese ran with outstretched necks from a doorway, attacking him noisily, one nipping his tail as he made a sudden exit from the yard, once again with his pride hurt much more than he was himself.

The Canada geese did not pursue him further than the yard confines, which they guarded as well as any dogs and much more cheaply. Old Red continued his run along one rut of two made by farm vehicles in the ancient green lane, once part of a network of paths to villages about the area. Here he came upon two rats burrowing under the wall of a shed where grain was stored and he killed them both before they knew of his coming. These were two brown rats born earlier in the year and thus they still had not learned the great cunning and experience of older rats, nor would they.

The fox ate one, which had attained eight inches in the body and almost that length in the tail, then leaving the other he moved back the way he had come.

From the galvanised iron roof of a shed a brown falcon with slate-grey head flew to alight upon the remaining rat, which still struggled in its death throes; the bird, believing it had killed the animal, pecked it hard behind the head as if delivering the final death blow.

The male kestrel then flew with his easy pickings, passing Old Red to enter the loft of one of the farm outbuildings where his mate sat on three richly coloured brown and cream eggs. Calling to her with a high pitched 'kee-kee-keee', he dropped the rat in the dry straw as she came to eat it readily, whereupon the male settled himself to continue the incubation of their eggs.

Old Red meanwhile had reached the farmyard. He paused in the shadow of a building, remembering the Canada geese. They were in the centre of the yard by an old iron water pump which still worked water up from a well. One dozed in the last sunny spot before sunset, its head buried beneath one wing, the other bird preening its breast feathers, its black neck arched as it did so, unaware of Old Red's return.

The fox savoured the moment, the grin on his face widening as his mouth opened to reveal his sharp white teeth and long red tongue.

Suddenly he dashed headlong into the yard, the geese panicking, honking loudly as the peace was shattered by the fox's charge. They rose to fly blindly into the walls and a farm cart resting on its end, sending chickens which had been feeding nearby scattering high and low. One came to rest in the loft window where the female kestrel, disturbed from her rat supper, screamed in anger, raking the chicken with her talons as it flew squawking in panic back into the yard.

As buckets, a spade and a rake clattered from where they had rested neatly against a wall, struck by flying fowls, a man dashed out from the largest building shouting, 'Has the world gone bloody mad?!'

He stopped to survey the scene, the ruffled geese pacing agitatedly about, the chickens slinking into whatever cover they could find, and he scratched his head for he could see no reason for the commotion.

Already a quarter of a mile away, Old Red trotted homeward towards the setting sun, happy with his excursion into new territory, happier still with the chicken raked by the talons of the kestrel which had fallen before his nose as he ran through the farmyard, and which now rested in his jaws as he neared his Tutshill home.

Of Mute Swans

***

The Taw estuary stretched wide from Ashford Strand across to the south bank where lay the large green expanse of Penhill marshes. The river gleamed silvery, lying placid on the turn of a spring tide, gently heaving and surging against its banks like some huge glistening serpent, as if breathing deeply as it lapped; waiting for the ebb to drain the vast channel of sand and mud for the second time that day.

Old Red had wandered from Tutshill Woods along the length of the Bradiford Water without sighting a rat, vole or any other likely meal. Now he prowled the Ashford shoreline in ever hopeful expectancy, the true opportunist hunter. Ahead of him in the twilight a grey heron stalked the inner gulley, which ran parallel to the old railway along which the fox had fled long ago from his birthplace at Braunton Burrows. The heron's long spindly legs waded slowly through the brackish water as it searched for fish or other prey. A wolf spider hunting its own prey along the railway embankment scuttled back into its retreat tube as Old Red's shadow fell silently upon it. The fox pushed by the white flowers of water parsnip and nosed through dense reeds to find an open stretch of fresh water on which a drake and duck mallard dabbled, oblivious to the presence of the lone hunter.

Old Red lowered his belly to watch them hungrily. The two mallard fed on, keeping to the centre of the pool but nowhere was the water less than two-feet deep and the fox knew he could not reach them before they flew free. From the dense reeds close to the fox's head came the loud, hurried song of a sedge warbler, the mix of musical and harsh notes spreading out across the marshes to merge with the songs of others nesting nearby. Old Red drew back into the reeds, leaving the ducks feeding quietly, to move lithely through rank vegetation. A cock reed bunting flicked his face with one wing as it flew up from where it had been feeding on insects, alighting high on a velvety reedmace head; below, its mate sat close on five eggs in a cup-shaped nest of dried grasses, sedge and hair.

The fox skirted the pond edge, his feet splashing through the shallows, a large greenish toad jumping from his path as he approached a rising piece of ground and more dense vegetation. Old Red saw the gleam of white through the reeds as he broke cover on to a small pond adjoining that upon which the mallard fed. There upon the water, wings half raised as he bore down upon the fox, was Cygnus the cob mute swan and behind him his mate of four years with their five downy cygnets. Old Red bared his fangs as the large white bird closed on him hissing loudly, a quarter-hundredweight of meat, bone and feather sweeping through the water in anger at this invasion of his family's privacy and territory. Old Red held his ground, feeling fear. The bird's bulk blocked out the sunlight as it waddled out of the pond to strike at him with open hissing bill, catching the fox's nose sharply with a sickening blow. Old Red yelped, turning sideways to parry a second stroke, which missed him. The swan hurled himself on to the fox, Old Red twisting away, his brain telling him it was not worth risking injury against so powerful an adversary, and he moved hurriedly away leaving the bird triumphant. A while later Old Red caught and ate a large rat in Poleshill Lane whereupon he sought the shade of a giant oak at the lane end and fell promptly asleep within its root cover.

For the remainder of that night the fox slept thus, awakening to the sound of metal upon stones, and men's voices close by him. He rose, keeping to the cover of nettles and brambles beneath a clump of trees where the earth was much turned over by people hunting for old bottles, once rubbish, now collectors' pieces upon many a mantleshelf.

He climbed the bank, which dropped sheer and ivy-covered to the road below, crouching as he saw workmen toiling at the task of removing earth and rocks from one side of the entrance to Halls Mill Lane.

The men were creating a visibility splay here to give motorists a clearer view on to main road. The work went on for another hour, Old Red choosing to wait rather than detour across country, lying with his forelegs stretched before him upon a soft carpet of moss, well-hidden by bluebells growing tall from the rich soil. A hedgehog appeared beside him, the fox watching it wander slowly and deliberately down on to the stony bank, then tumble, rolling to the road and out upon it where it lay inert for brief moments. Then it uncurled to continue on its leisurely way through the staring group of workmen and on down Halls Mill Lane.

'Time for a break lads,' one of the men called and downing his pick he stared about him as he lit a cigarette. Work ceased and Old Red watched the group gather on his side of the road where the Poleshill Lane entrance afforded a better place to sit to linger over the lunch-break. The fox rose and stretched, looking along the bank to where soil erosion had made an easy drop to the roadside. A car passed by and with its passing he dropped to the tarmac, heading after the hedgehog which crouched still as Old Red trotted by it, then resumed its own steady way after the fox. A pair of pied wagtails flew before him along the lane, almost moth-like in their undulating flight, and the fox chased after them for the sheer fun of it, grinning as they flew high, then back, over his tawny-red form to perch near their nest in a crevice formed by two fallen stones against an old gatepost.

At Anchor Mill a dog the colour of the wagtails' plumage leapt up to run the full length of his chain, to be brought up snarling and snapping as Old Red ran up behind the mill, passing the pit where once an undershot mill wheel had worked the machinery within. Old Red ran along the track towards Yarnerwood Cottage, behind him the sound of the dog still barking. Now two fields away, the fox ran into a family of shelduck, a female and nine downy young, cheep-cheeping their way to the estuary over a mile away. The shelduck had been born in a rabbit burrow close to Tutshill woods, their parents in their third year of breeding at this site. The female attacked Old Red so ferociously he did not take advantage of the possible meal, passing through the little group on the run, his encounter with the mute swan still etched boldly on his mind.

Old Red had had enough of daylight hunting. He was learning the wisdom of hunting at night or at least in the dusk and dawn times of the day, as had Lutra the otter and others of their kind even though their ancestors were day hunters.

A chiffchaff called above Old Red as he drank deeply from the stream where it joined the leat above an old rusty sluice gate. A moorhen called its almost metallic cry from a nest along the leat but Old Red paid no heed as he left the water's edge, shaking sparkling droplets from his chin before heading up through the woods to his earth and peace.

Of Fish and Hare and Things

•◆•

The white stars of greater stitchwort shone along the hedge bank leading from Old Red's earth down over the hill slope, like a white mist floating over the greenery.

Shaded by trees the stitchwort grew well here whilst in amongst its whiteness the pointed leaves and purple spadix of wild arum or parson in the pulpit thrust into the moist air, attracting female moth flies to climb inside to aid the plant's pollination.

On this balmy spring evening Old Red trotted along the field edge, pausing as the sound of scratching came from a small stand of trees ahead of him. He waited and the sound came again.

The fox placed his forepaws amongst the stitchwort, raising himself to peer over the hedge bank into the trees. There on its hind legs was a badger scraping its claws on one of the tree trunks, the bark scored and scarred with the marks of Brock and his family who lived in a large sett nearby as their kind had done for two centuries. Old Red watched as the boar badger tore a small piece of bark from a tree on the other side of the clump of oaks with its teeth, biting at the bark and then licking the exuding sap with obvious relish.

Old Red moved on. He did not bother the badgers, nor they him, though on at least two occasions he had laid up in their sett to avoid humans.

A sudden outburst of song from the darkening hedge gave away the hiding place of a dunnock. Nearby in the depths of the bushes his mate peeped with sleep-filled eyes from her newly built nest. Her mate, singing into the night now as he often did in the springtime, had courted her all day on quivering wings, flitting from twig to twig with continuous piping calls. Now she rested after mating, soon to lay her clutch of beautifully coloured blue eggs.

Old Red paid scant attention to the sudden outburst of song from the little brown bird. To him it was a sign that all was well so he moved on, loping now into the fields of Blakewell and beyond, where the setting sun turned the patchwork of meadows golden with its light.

A mewing cry and Buteo the great brown buzzard hawk soared majestically out over the valley from the woods to swing round in a wide arc, its last flight of the day before going to roost in the oaks of Tutshill woods. Below him the hawk saw Old Red trot up over the hillside to sit and survey the valley below him, the fox's keen eyes becoming accustomed to the gloom, the buzzard's losing their keenness in the fading light. The hawk circled the valley once, then holding his wings close in to his body, dived for the trees where he would stay until daybreak.

The setting sun poised blood red above the brow of the westward hills then dipped towards the unseen sea, tipping the treetops with liquid fire for brief moments before plunging the land into darkness and shadow. Now Old Red was in his element, the night hunter, whereas Buteo and other birds of the day already slept, like all diurnal birds, captives of the darkness. The fox glanced around him letting his eyes adjust, seeing more clearly the shapes about him. He twitched his nose, pointing his ears and learning of the night creatures he could not see.

A field mouse squeaked and Old Red's immediate pounce took him clear of the ground, landing with all four feet together as the mouse bounded into a hole amongst the grasses and was safely lost to the darkness. The fox sniffed at the hole entrance then moved away along the field edge after drinking from water forming a small pool fed by a spring, the day place of blackbirds and thrushes who drank and bathed here.

A new scent caught his nostrils, wafting on the breeze from a gateway leading into Blakewell Mill Road. Old Red followed the scent-line, ears forward, nostrils twitching, moving silently on gently placed paws as dark as the night. Another more pungent scent mingled with the first and Old Red stiffened, hackles rising, for the smell of petrol was distasteful to him. Humans!

Again all his senses alerted him to caution but the original scent that had attracted his attention wafted to his nostril causing his mouth to water. He padded forward and immediately found the source of the scent, a piece of paper held fast by the weight of half a portion of fried fish. Old Red sniffed, licked, then ate the food quickly, wolfing the tasty fish and several fried chips lying beside the paper which now drifted away on the breeze. Voices and the movement of shadows by the gateway caused him to crouch and retreat into the darkness of the high hedge. He watched as two men entered the field, one an annoyed young man who had earlier suffered a sharp fish bone in the roof of his mouth and had tossed away the remains of his meal in anger. The fox watched them stand surveying the fields, his body still, though he licked his lips still savouring the taste of the food he had just eaten.

'Are you sure we'll see any?' said the fish-bone man, and then, 'Blast!' as his shoes squelched into the mess of a recent cowpat.

'Not your night is it?' grinned his companion, a man more used to the countryside at night. It was he who had reluctantly agreed to show the other badgers for the first time and was already regretting it though amused at the same time. He now led the way across the field watched by Old Red's keen eyes, the two men climbing a chained and padlocked gate to disappear into the next field. The fox waited for a while before following on the same route, slipping under the familiar gateway to move at a lope across the badger field. Away in a field corner the two men sat on a bracken-covered hump of ground giving full views of the large mound of the badger sett with dark entrance holes visible along it, and the shadowy copse beyond.

'Do you think we'll see anything tonight?' asked the fish-bone man again of his quiet companion.

'Not if you natter away all night,' was the whispered reply and in a way he rather did not mind if they saw nothing of the badgers. The evening was pleasantly mild, the night sounds and fresh air a delight to his senses.

He gazed across the field where he had spent many hours watching wildlife, seeing Old Red loping in the distance. 'Fox,' he whispered pointing, the breeze in his face telling him the fox would not scent them. They watched the animal move on across the field and leap into the hedge in the distance. Old Red stood poised on the hedge bank on short grass beneath a huge oak, looking back across the route he had travelled, seeing the two watchers on the hillside too far distant to worry him.

A half-moon had risen high, the light falling from it the quarter of a million miles to earth, showing the fox the hare-path he followed and the place where the hare using this route leapt some twelve feet from the grassy meadow to leave no tracks for its enemies. Often Old Red had watched it run at speed with great bounds across the fields, knowing these animals would make a tasty meal if caught though he chased easier prey from choice, as did all intelligent predators.

Hares had held a stable population in this area of countryside, increasing slightly in numbers when myxomatosis greatly reduced the rabbit population in the 1950s. Hares will not usually feed where rabbits dwell and moreover buck rabbits would go about the fields with young hares in them and kill the animals.

Now Old Red scanned the field, seeing a brown hare feeding in the distance on the lush vegetation. A female, she lived here at Blakewell in a favourite form between two horse chestnut trees.

The fox watched her feeding, hopping from one choice spot to another, eating grass and the occasional spring mushroom head, feeding hurriedly. He dropped lightly from the bank, his feet holding the scent of spring flowers as he slunk low across the field until. when within a few yards of the unsuspecting hare, he rushed her at top speed.

The hare, at that moment hopping from one mushroom to the next, leapt high in the air to run off with Old Red in hot pursuit. She ran in a great circle about the field then leaping again ran in a tighter circle, then another, the fox racing all the while but losing ground, his handsome face staring, tongue lolling, as he watched this strange quarry which ran so swiftly. Realising the hare was losing him and performing another arc, Old Red cut across the circle and drew to within a yard of her upon which she promptly leapt again, eyes rolling, directly over the hedge bank ten feet ahead of her.

Old Red ran to the bank, jumping upon it to see the hare bounding across the next field towards the stream below Blakewell Mill where there was an old orchard in which she sometimes hid. She ran as all hares do placing her long hind legs before her forelegs, reaching forward to cover the ground much faster than any rabbit and was soon finding safe cover in the darkness of the orchard.

The fox, meanwhile, was already heading back towards his home ground where prey would be easier to find. His fish and chip supper would stay with him until the morrow, the hare already dismissed from his mind as is the way of wild creatures.

Of Summer Days and Humans

◦◆◦

Old Red had been basking in the hot June sunshine since the sun had first burnt off the morning mist from the valley, chin laid on forepaws as he gazed with half-open eyes at the stream tumbling over shining stones below him. He lay between hawthorn and gorse bushes in full flower at the wood edge where it joined the rabbit field. His eyes were dazed by the flickering sunlight that dappled and flashed, the water white and yellow with summer colours where it chattered over stones that had known many of his kind over the centuries.

A dragonfly hawked above the water surface, its brilliant apple-green and blue body and clear sparkling wings catching Old Red's eyes, waking him from his drowsing as he watched the large insect zoom after midges. Another flew before him in the wake of the first, an all-green female following her more colourful mate upstream. The two *Southern Aeshnaes* had emerged as nymphs from the water above the weir under the woods two days before, becoming perfect flying insects in a matter of hours, drying in the hot sunshine that had warmed the valley for the past several days. Now they hawked small insects along the sunlit waters as Old Red watched them lazily. The first grasshopper of the year chirped loudly from a stem of wood millet and from somewhere close by a willow warbler sang its sweet descending trilling song to the world.

Sounds other than those of the tumbling waters and insects caught Old Red's ears and he looked up and through the vegetation without moving.

'Bramble! Bramble, where are you? Come here boy!' A voice called as Old Red watched the lone figure of a tall young woman stride towards him along the middle path in the woods. A dog barked close by and the fox was immediately alert as he watched the woman be joined by a black and white collie larger than he, the dog barking again as it ran to its owner to drop a stick at her feet.

'Shush Bramble, good boy,' the woman called, ignoring the stick and pausing, catching her breath as she did so as she looked into the eyes of Old Red who was now standing just to one side of the path she and her dog were on. All three pairs of eyes stared, the woman, the dog and the fox glancing from one to the other for long moments. Then Old Red turned away to move up over the wood slope, the dog barking again as he gave chase. Old Red ran amongst the brambles and ferns beneath the trees, into a clearing where two ancient beeches had fallen long ago, turning to see the dog scrambling head down through the undergrowth, bursting into view, eyes rolling with excitement, tongue lolling.

'Bramble! Bramble!' The woman called to the dog but to no avail, seeing the collie race amongst the trees with the fox just ahead of him. Old Red ran along the main pathway down through hazel, young oaks and sycamores to the stream, dashing across the shallows and along the stony bank, then back into the wood to find the collie close behind him. There was no anger in either, the dog no hunter of foxes but willing to chase and play, his every instinct telling him to chase, but he had no instinct to kill or maim.

The woman, amazed and amused by the sight, stood against a tree to watch. She knew the fox was master here and though her dog was fast and ran hither and thither he at no time closed to within more than a body length of his quarry. Then, much to the amazement of the woman watcher the fox turned in his play, chasing the collie who ran barking amongst the trees, leaping over fallen logs with the fox in hot pursuit. And so for long moments the two played their own game of tag amongst the trees, watched by the transfixed and enchanted woman until Old Red, suddenly finding himself at her feet and seeing her beside him, ran away up into the deeper shadows of the high trees, leaving behind a disappointed woman and equally disappointed but breathless dog. Minutes later Old Red slowed as he neared his earth, breathing easily still in the cool shade of the great trees of this ancient woodland.

Passing beneath hazel forming a green tunnel to within thirty paces of his lair, Old Red suddenly sensed danger, whirling from his route too late to avoid a crashing blow behind his ears, the world going red then black before his eyes as he fell upon the pathway.

'I've got it! I've got it!' shouted the larger of two youths, who was holding a heavy branch with which he had just felled the fox. 'Never thought I'd get 'n', he said and the two stared down at the unconscious fox lying limply before them.

The younger of the two youths stared down in dismay at the animal. So beautiful, it had been trotting through the trees and now it lay with closed eyes, broken neck fur and heaving sides as it breathed heavily before him. He felt shame and anger surging through him. He had failed to stop his friend striking the fox more in expectation that he would miss, not believing the fox would fail to avoid the blow. His eyes were hot and misted over as he knelt beside the animal.

'What are you going to do?' asked the older youth as he tossed the branch away into the bushes.

'Oh shut up!' came the reply and the younger lad picked Old Red up in his arms, holding him tightly as he stumbled off down over the wooded hillside, the fox a dead weight against his chest.

At the side of the stream he laid the fox in the high grass, looking up to find the young woman and her dog suddenly beside him, the dog held firmly on a leash.

'Oh my God!' she exclaimed, 'Whatever has happened?'

The youth explained while the woman tied her dog to a sapling where it sat whining and puzzled but obedient, watching his mistress and the youth crouching over the fox.

Old Red lay close to the water's edge on grasses and buckler fern as he came to, feeling water trickling into his mouth. He opened his eyes on hearing human voices, lying staring at blurred visions of movement. Then more water trickled into his mouth causing him to splutter and lift his head, which ached. He lay back on the cool vegetation and rested, feeling his head being stroked. It was soothing and quiet. Voices entered his brain. The woman bathed Old Red's head using her headscarf soaked in water from the stream.

'Come on old boy,' she coaxed as her heart gladdened to see the fox open his eyes again and to know there was no real wound, just a bruising where the blow from the branch had struck him.

Old Red sat up, the woman and the youth stepping back against the trees to watch as the collie barked and whined to be near his play friend. Old Red stood and shook himself, stumbling for a brief moment and then walking to the stream where he drank long and deeply.

As he dipped once more into the freshening water, his eyes focussing sharply now, he turned to stare about him. The collie was watching, tail wagging and whining excitedly as the fox stared hard at the three, looking into the eyes of each in turn before moving quietly away along the stream bank where he again drank water, standing shoulder deep in the clear stream. The three companions watched him leave the stream, shake his coat free of water, overjoyed as he sprayed them and the surrounding vegetation with myriad droplets. Old Red gave them one last look then was up and into the denser undergrowth the incident already behind him.

'How perfectly lovely,' said the woman. 'I hope you will always treat animals this way young man,' and she smiled at the youth as they made their way out of the woods together.

Old Red lay outside his earth entrance staring sleepily down over the open field adjoining the woods. He watched wood pigeons fly up and away in an arc, seeing the two humans and the collie he had played with crossing the field to the lane bottom. He saw the wood pigeons settle in the clover as they left, saw swallows, martins and swifts skimming above the trees. Then sleep overcame him, and time, the two great healers of the natural world. Old Red lay undreaming, his head resting on cool grasses, his lithe body stretched peacefully beneath the summer trees where sweet woodruff and wood avens were the bed upon which he lay.

Of Dunnocks, Cuckoos and a River Journey

•◆•

Old Red had recovered swiftly from his cruel treatment at the hands of the youth. Though slightly bruised, he was his old self within a day or so of the incident occurring, having rested up in the woods for the whole of a day and a night to awake hungry on a dry and pleasant summer's eve.

He sat scratching behind one ear with a hind leg, his keen eyes taking in the scene about him.

A family of jays flitted noisily from branch to branch deep in the woods, flashing their white rumps as they flew, showing the pinks and blues of bright plumage, the brightest of the crow family. Blackbirds scuffed the dead-leaf cover from the woodland soil in their search for food as bees hummed along the main path, glowing gold and silver where their fat bodies and wings caught the light from the evening sun.

A lesser spotted woodpecker flew by the fox, alighting on a fallen gean tree, a wild cherry, which still blossomed each year and bore fruit, for its roots had remained in the woodland soil when it fell. The little black and white bird tapped away at the tree's trunk for a while then flew high into the canopy where its mate had a nest in the dead branch of an oak. Old Red followed his own path to the fallen gean then took a wider path to the steeply sloping weir field with its terraces of sheep tracks running horizontally along it. A pair of dunnocks flew up from the hedge bank to become hidden as the fox passed their nest within a hazel stand. Both birds uttered their prolonged alarm notes 'tseep, tsee-eep' over and over as the fox drew closer to their hiding place overlooking a dense patch of nettles that grew out into the field from the side of the bank.

Old Red came to the nettle patch to hear shuffling sounds beyond. Immediately his hunting instincts were fully alert for he was hungry. The sounds came again and the alarm notes of the dunnocks became more urgent as the fox crouched, tensing before dashing straight through the nettles on to the back of a large reddish-brown bird with strongly marked barring in its plumage. The fox bit into the white patch at the bird's nape and it died without a sound as the two dunnocks flew, still calling, into the wood edge amongst shrub cover.

During the month of June the female dunnock had laid four clear blue eggs in the nest she had built by herself in the hazel thicket. This was her second clutch of the year, she and her mate having raised one successful brood of five youngsters since their April mating. One afternoon, with the fourth egg freshly laid, she had left the nest briefly and while away had heard the call of a male cuckoo at the wood edge. With her mate and a pair of blue tits she had harassed a large grey bird until it flew low over the field, hedge-hopping away to be followed by the female cuckoo, which had appeared from the hedgerow. The female dunnock had returned to her nest, settling to incubate her eggs for the next thirteen days, never knowing that the female cuckoo had flown from her very nest, or that one of her own eggs lay hidden below her in the nettles where it had been dropped as the large visitor from Africa had laid an egg of her own in the nest of the dunnocks.

And so, on the twelfth day, a young female cuckoo was born to dunnock hosts and she had quickly set about ejecting the dunnock young on their day of hatching, laboriously raising them on her naked shoulders to eject them over the side of the nest.

For a further twenty-one days the two adult dunnocks flew to and from the nest, feeding the cuckoo until she filled the whole nest cup, then on the twenty-first day of her life she had flapped her wings at the evening sun, falling to the ground where her adopted parents had continued to feed her voracious appetite. She had taken every morsel offered, calling for more, shuffling about in the herbage as her wings strengthened.

Hearing the alarm calls of the two dunnocks, yet still demanding more food, she did but briefly hear the rush of Old Red's body through the nettle bed before he was upon her and she heard no more.

The two dunnocks, feathers worn and daily exhausted by their valiant efforts to feed the young cuckoo, watched the fox eat where he stood, leaving the feathers, head and feet to tell the story to others who passed this way.

Later, as the summer's day was ending in a blaze of glorious colour, Old Red was in an open field beyond Blakewell, having wandered far across country exploring as he sought a more substantial meal. Long summer days meant shorter nights and dew was heavy upon the grasses where long tree shadows reached across the field like outstretched hands. The fox ran out into the last of the sunshine, leaping high into the air then leaping and twisting again, his lithe red body glowing as he performed agile contortions in mid-air to catch and eat crane flies hatching from the leatherjackets hidden in sun-kissed soil. He took many of these before moving on, nosing along the hedgerow to come to a gateway leading into an old orchard.

Here he paused to watch an old toad sitting in front of a wasp's nest, which bulged greyly from a hole in the hedge bank. Each time a wasp appeared at the nest entrance the toad's tongue flicked out, the insects disappearing into the toad's capacious stomach.

Tiring of toad-watching and knowing they made a bad meal for one of his kind, Old Red trotted across the orchard filled now with deep orange light and purple shadows, to leap through a gap in the hedge into a marsh field where he splashed through shallow water, reaching a log across a swollen stream which here was deep and swift-flowing. Old Red stepped lightly upon it, feeling it judder and move beneath his feet for the log did not fully reach the opposite bank.

Old Red gazed across. The opposite bank was low and there were rabbits in the field. He took a further step, all four feet firmly placed. With a crack the one root holding the log in place snapped, soft earth pouring into the water as the fox found himself floating downstream on the swift current, his legs braced to steady himself as he lowered his body instinctively against the tree bark. The log swung in an arc as it tore from the stream bank, the heavier root end heading into the current, Old Red now hurtling along tail first, his startled eyes seeing the receding scenery before him.

He turned his head, looking along his red back to see where he was going. A clump of trees rushed at him then were gone as the log swept around a bend in the stream where it picked up the flow from the Colam Water, almost dislodging the fox as it briefly struck the roots of alders and swept on again. He felt overhanging brambles harshly brush his coat, striking his head and he closed his eyes fearing harder blows as the log rushed through white water, rocking as it reached a slower-flowing meandering part of the waterway. The fox looked about him. On one side there were trees, on the other an open field. He recognised the mink lair and heard the roaring of the weir as the log picked up speed beneath the trees of his home woodland, swiftly approaching the four-foot drop of water flashing white and sparkling, where only days before he had swum joyfully. The log entered the deep mirror of water above the weir, striking the iron fittings of old sluice machinery, swinging about and throwing Old Red into the water. He rose spluttering, swimming for the bank as with scrabbling forepaws he hauled himself from the weir pool, hearing the crashing sounds of the log as it tipped and went over to become jammed in the shallows below.

Old Red scrambled panting on to the bank of the leat, his coat clinging to his lean body. Shaking himself he padded up over the weir top, none the worse for his experience, following the path up through his beloved woodland and home.

Of Smokey House Lane

◆

Two days of summer rain had swept across the valley, coming in from the sea and along the estuary of the Taw and Torridge to reach Exmoor's high ground.

Old Red had not hunted for the rain had fallen heavier by night. He was hungry and now, with the passing of the rain, he watched Buteo soaring low over the fields beyond his earth, the hawk seeking food for his mate who was brooding young, keeping their downy forms as dry as she was able in their stick nest high in the eastward corner of the woods.

All day the sun had warmed the valley, drying the grasslands and hedgerows as wood and farmland birds sang or sought food for their young and themselves, for there were many nests in the valley at this time. Along the rain-swollen leat, moorhens with eight young strutted proudly in front of their inky-black downy charges. They had hurriedly built up their nest height with the coming of the rain, avoiding the flood of suddenly rising water which had almost reached the dipper's nest built beneath the old stone bridge arch near the entrance to the woods.

The dippers had flown three fields downstream from their nest site to find a clear pool in which to collect food for their own six young, the rain bringing sediment down from the moors that coloured the water for two days. Now they were able to plunge beneath the waters of the weir pool once more to catch and carry food but a matter of paces to where their nestlings clamoured for sustenance. The young, just three weeks old, would stay in the nest for a further four days or so before fledging, to dive with their parents for food before they were able to fly properly. The older birds would continue to feed them for some time, skimming about the waterway as a family group for several weeks in their half-mile territory.

Old Red had passed the place of the dippers, his hunger driving him to seek a good meal, the evening sun's warmth a stimulus as much as was the hunger in his belly, and now he was heading down a steep hill slope above the tiny hamlet of Raleigh. Here, as he loped along a short track with iron gates at each end, the sharp 'crack' of an air rifle and the lead pellet hitting a tree beside his head had him running to lose the gang of youths who had chased after him with much shouting and waving of arms.

He had run on along the Yeo Valley, hiding in a derelict barn where a rat and two mice had filled his belly, all caught within the falling walls of the building which now housed only the hidden nets and snares of poachers who lived in the housing estate on the edge of the nearby town. Not liking the feel of the place, Old Red had left the building to follow the River Yeo upstream where more shooting had driven him on to find a disused earth by Collard Bridge. Here he hid, dozing, as the sounds of shooting gradually ceased, the poachers taking their spoils to their various homes.

The rustling noise of a tawny owl catching a field mouse not a yard before his eyes awoke the fox from his dozing. He rose from hiding, trotting out on to the road which led to the village of Loxhore, to follow a lane where a concrete pipe carried water away from the place called Snapper. Old Red trotted along the wide pathway of Smokey House Lane, named of charcoal burning days when the smoke from the fires could be seen along its route for miles around. He reached the high-walled gardens of a lone house where he caught and ate a bank vole as it ate peas in the well-tended garden, chasing two others which dived into holes in a wall holding apple racks, and were gone.

Old Red nosed along a row of bean sticks and finding no voles he ate strawberries from lush green plants, disturbing a mouse, which ran beneath glass cloches and was lost. He sniffed his way along the wall bottom until a light went on in the upstairs window of the house, Old Red running from the rectangle of light thrown on to the soil at his feet. He ran on along the grassy route, passing a quarry where sparrowhawks lived in a stick nest built low in a tree at its entrance, coming to a part of the lane with no trees, seeing the Yeo Valley beneath him shrouded with mist as behind him the sun began to rise on another day.

Above Pitt Farm he paused as a cock pheasant flew from the hedge bank where it had slept the night on the lowest branch of an oak, calling as it flew then landing to begin its early morning strut about the field edges. The fox did not give chase but moved on to where a sharp bend in the lane led steeply up to Roborough Road. Here the going was wet, Old Red splashing through watercress which grew thickly, topped by white flowers lying pillow-like above the water surface, the lane fed by many springs, where lived water shrews, tiny black and white mammals of these secret waterways. At the lane top a song thrush was smashing a snail upon an anvil stone about which were strewn many shells of past meals. The bird flew up into the bank as Old Red passed, returning immediately to its task as the fox turned the corner into Roborough Road to lope downhill, hurrying now as the sun rose higher.

He reached the north road leading into the ancient market town, already busy with traffic, trotting along a grassy verge at Westaway and crossing the road unseen to move down the private road to Playford Mill. An elderly woman watched him cross the field to the woods, smiling happily to herself as he paused to drink from the stream below the weir before splashing across in the morning sunlight. She picked a few more sprigs of sorrel, or sour dock as she called it, placing it in her canvas bag with other herbs carefully chosen from the hedgerows. She would use them for making green sauce to eat with fish, pulping the leaves and mixing them with vinegar and sugar. The fox ignored her for he often saw her here on good weather days and knew she was of no harm to him.

Once at his earth he lay down, chin on outstretched forelegs, letting the warming sun lull him to sleep.

Midsummer

◆

Along midsummer day with much human activity in the valley had meant a late start to Old Red's hunting for he had grown fond of finding enough to eat by day, even on the early evenings when the valley was quiet. Hungry now, he had lain in brambles at the wood edge, biding his time until all was quiet. He watched the back of a farmworker disappear into the field by the bottom of Shearford Lane, knowing the man was making his way back to Westaway and the farm buildings, that he would not be returning until the sun rose again. Old Red rose from his hiding place, trotting to the Bradiford Water where he drank deeply then swam across just to enjoy the feeling of the cold water cleaning the dust from his hot body.

The fox clambered on to the opposite bank shaking his coat free of water, watching gatekeeper and meadow brown butterflies fluttering before him about the grasses that were the homes for their eggs. He sniffed about the steps of a new bridge that spanned the water, smelling humans and dogs that had passed this way earlier, knowing they were not about the fields and that the way along his favourite route was unimpeded. He trotted up Shearford Lane along the top path where a robin sang sweetly into the evening to four speckled young crouched in the buckler ferns ten feet below him. They were by the stream of water created by surface water run-off from the fields, fed also by several springs, a place of many birds and small mammals who drank here unseen and undisturbed by human activity.

A sparrowhawk, seeing movement amongst the herbage, poised to attack but on seeing the fox the golden-eyed predator launched from its oak-tree branch perch to hedge-hop across the fields to Westaway Farm. Here was a pond which attracted birds to bathe and drink, forgetting for brief moments that there might be sparrowhawks about.

A treecreeper flitted to the lower part of an oak growing beside a dead elm destroyed by beetle attack many years before, beginning its spiralling search for insects upwards and around the bole of the tree. The huge elm, having been killed by Dutch Elm disease along with all the others in the valley and beyond, now jutted starkly towards the summer sky, no longer leaf covered and green as in its one hundred summers of life before man's vehicles had driven the birds from the hedgerows; the birds the predators of the elm bark beetles which had ravaged the trees to destruction.

Old Red reached the half-way point along the route, sniffing at two rabbit holes dug from the hedge bank, but there was no meal here and he moved on to Maer Top and the main road.

All was quiet as the fox trotted close to the hedge, making his way to the North Road, down along the sloping grass verge dividing the footpath from the old waterworks site, trotting on past the wall into which a Second World War aircraft had crashed in the 1940s; many people had come to stare and to take away souvenirs from close to where the body of the pilot lay crouched in a cockpit engulfed by fire. The fox ran on over a pathway where a meteorite had fallen at much the same time as the aircraft, burying itself in the ground and leaving a crater for little boys and girls and their parents to stare and wonder at, until it was filled in with rubble and covered with tar.

Old Red did not know he had passed over the rock from another time and place, from millions of miles in space, the heavy rock still lying in the place where it had fallen to Earth all those years before. Even though it had borne deeply etched signs of life from another planet, it had made litle impact on those who had seen it fall, had heard the explosion of its landing, but were blind to its importance in the greater scheme of things.

Across the road two people walked, city holidaymakers from the north, the young man pursing his lips and whistling as he saw the fox pass on the other side. He clicked two fingers together but the fox went on. 'Funny looking dogs down here,' he said, his arm about his girlfriend.

'Yeah. Looked like one of them foxes we saw on the telly, don't you remember?' she said.

'Hmmm. No not in the daylight. They come out in the dark,' the man said as he turned to watch Old Red round the wide bend in the road and disappear from sight

The fox slipped through iron fencing, which stretched for a quarter of a mile down the road protecting the boundary of a number of allotment gardens into which he now made his way.

The fox found himself on the wide earth path used by all the allotment gardeners and now he slowed, taking each pace carefully, ears pricked forward, eyes staring and nose twitching for every scent. A bonfire lit the day before still smouldered, sending a stream of blue smoke high into the summer sky where swallows and house martins twittered as they ceaselessly hunted insects flying high over the gardens. The fox detoured widely around the fire site, coming to a row of sheds. He circled slowly around the first of these, smelling the scent of mice. His mouth watered as he nosed towards the second shed where an old zinc bath lay upside-down against one wall. He could smell wood mice now, knowing they were close. He placed a paw upon the old bath, peering beneath as he did so. Slight movement caught his eye and he pawed again, the bath sliding back against the shed wall with a crash. Mice suddenly swarmed on to the path, two dying as the fox leapt high to land amongst them, snapping as he did so. He ate them there, then nosed along a row of beans, catching and eating a third mouse before leaving the allotment under the five-barred gate opposite Higher Raleigh. Passing River View he was seen by a woman from her windows who dashed out brandishing an umbrella for no real reason, amazing a passer-by who had not seen the fox leap the hedge bank into the overgrown gardens of an old dairy.

'I was chasing a fox,' muttered the woman by way of explanation to the passing stranger who hurried on wondering at the strange hunting methods employed by the locals hereabouts.

Along the pathway of the old dairy garden, Old Red came across the little black kidney-shaped stomachs of two voles left by a cat who had caught and ate the remainder earlier. He sniffed at these then saw an egg laid by a free-ranging hen on the grass against the stone wall. He ate the egg, leaving the broken shell licked clean. Above him, from the eaves of the old dairy roof, a stream of pipistrelle bats flew into the swiftly fading light as they sought insect food. Old Red glanced up at them until they were swallowed by the gathering darkness, then went on his way through the garden area, around the house and down a flight of stone steps to Littabourne Road.

The fox glanced about him and seeing no one about he loped up the hill to Gravel Path, leaping the steps there to follow the high tree-lined route above the roadway.

With the gathering darkness the pale disc-like blossoms of elder lit the hedgerows, the air still and soft, as a gentle breeze stirred wildflower scents; drops of dew forming as the air cooled and a reluctant mist spread its slow-moving way along the stream and leats, marking their routes to the night travellers.

Old Red followed Gravel Path almost to its end, turning to leap upon the high grassy bank where the soil lay bared by his passing on numerous occasions. He looked to right and left knowing the traffic dangers of the main road, then he leapt down onto the tarmac immediately opposite the entrance to Shearford Lane. He trotted across the road, passing the old plank seat where sat the young couple who had remarked on 'the strange dog' earlier but they were oblivious to him now. Ignoring them, Old Red made his way down along the lane to the valley, his former hunger quelled enough for him to sleep the night through.

Of Buzzards

·◆·

A long hot summer's day had kept Old Red lolling in the shade of the oak trees at the edge of the wood adjoining his earth. His view was across the wide field where his gaze was attracted to the sight of two rabbits, which had suddenly appeared in the middle of it, their heads bobbing from view as they ate then looked about and ate again.

Old Red's eyes narrowed, his mouth watering as he gazed about, gauging distances and the best way to reach them unseen. He waited long moments as the rabbits fed quietly, coming only a little closer as they did so. Behind them in the hedgerow at the other side of the field where the holes of their burrows were, was a row of six beech trees, heavy now with beech mast, the tree shadows reaching out across the field. Old Red rose soundlessly, disappearing into his earth entrance to come out into the wood whereupon he trotted swiftly through the trees to where the wood edge sloped down to the stream. Here he left the shelter of the trees to run along the outside of the hedge in the field itself, crouching for a moment as swallows and house martins zoomed about his head taking the insects he had set to flight in his passing. Reaching the field corner he raised himself on his hind legs to peer over the hedge bank, seeing the rabbits close by him several yards from their burrows.

The fox's mouth watered. He could almost taste them and he trotted now to the shelter of the six beeches where he paused beside the nearest. Picus the green woodpecker screamed his laughing call across the valley as he flew with undulating flight from the beech trees, flashing his green, yellow and scarlet plumage. Alighting on a dead ivy-covered trunk, he immediately set about his own search for the insects that were his food, the fox's arrival forgotten.

Old Red crouched low in the tree shadows, the grass cool against his belly as he edged forward, the rabbit's retreat already cut off. A large and shining blue fly perched on his nose, walking along it towards his eyes, Old Red snuffling loudly in annoyance. The two rabbits stopped eating and stared his way. He lay still his eyes staring into theirs, first one and then the other but they did not see his form beneath the trees, only the waving buckler ferns which grew in abundance above their burrows. The two rabbits began to play, hopping after each other in a small circle and Old Red arose, running out into the open field, his feet flying over the grass sward as he bore down upon them.

A sudden shadow sped over the fox, dark and silent. In the next moment he heard the beating of the air, feeling its rushing about his head as he threw himself sideways to avoid the great brown hawk swooping by him, its talons missing him by inches as the bird took the nearest rabbit then flew low across the field to take its prey up and into the tree above Old Red's lair.

Buteo the buzzard, soaring in wide circles on the thermals of warm air over the fields, had seen the two rabbits at the same time as Old Red rose from the ferny bank. Beginning his hunting swoop from a hundred feet above the beeches, he took his prey with ease once his decision was made, seeing the fox only just before his talons struck to grip and kill.

Now he dropped on to the oak branch close to the nest where he and his mate were raising three young hawks born more than a month earlier from eggs laid in the spring. In a few day's time the young would fly free though they would remain with their parents as a family group until the late autumn months had come.

Old Red, recovered from the surprise of Buteo's dive, stared after the buzzard, watching it fly into the trees with the dangling rabbit in its talons. A beetle trundled its lone way through the grass before him, the fox ignoring it. He trotted away towards his earth, the second rabbit lost to him in the rush of the buzzard's arrival and jumping on to the grassy bank he lay in the shade watching for the evening to come.

Across the field a rabbit rose from a patch of gorse where it had run head-long in its escape from the onrush of hawk and fox, and had lain too frightened to move until it heard a whitethroat singing from the hawthorns and nettles nearby, and knew all was safe.

Old Red's keen eyes saw it rise and he watched it quietly as it lolloped the few yards to its burrow to vanish within. He did not move save to settle himself more snugly on the hedge bank to await the setting of the sun and a better time for hunting.

Of Fire

•◆•

'Come along children, do hurry up!'

A young woman's loud voice jarred upon Old Red's ears as he lay, a silent shadow in the shady depths of a dense tangle of gorse growing in the bottom of a long-disused quarry. He had found this place to lay up after a night of wandering and a heavy meal of fresh rabbit killed in a field of dewy grass that glittered in the light cast by the first rays of the rising sun.

The old quarry lay just off a well-used road leading to the village of Muddiford and was a place of picnickers and lovers wanting solitude for their respective pursuits.

Old Red had slept well into the day, awakened by the 'seee-chak! seee-chak!' of a male stonechat whose mate and family of four tiny nestlings lay low in a nest well-hidden in the grass beneath the gorse, just a yard from the fox's head. Old Red had lain dozing, then half-listening to the play-sounds of the humans whose arrival had caused the stonechat to warn his mate of their presence. Two hours passed by and the afternoon sun blazed hot on the family who played ball and picnicked on the rabbit-grazed turf beyond the gorse tangle. Now, after half an hour's rest in the sunshine, the woman was busily packing a basket with the picnic utensils, scattering the grass with crumbs and spare cake for the birds.

'Children. At once!' The woman's voice was impatient now and Old Red pointed his ears in her direction, his white chin resting on the dry soil beneath gorse stalks, flowerless and brown after days without rain. He licked his dry lips, watching one child racing towards her mother as she recognised the tone of voice that said to hurry meant just that. Her brother chased after her, his spirits high, full of mischief, for these were summer holidays away from school and his ten-year-old head was free of maths and science and the watching stare of his tutors. He saw the glint of a bottle shine amongst some quarry spoil and on impulse he reached down, swinging the old bottle by the neck to send it crashing against the quarry face. The noise of shattering glass was a sound alien to the usually peaceful place.

'Peter!' The boy temporarily left the ground as his irate mother grabbed him by one arm and he was yanked unceremoniously towards a waiting vehicle parked discreetly in the quarry entrance.

'Don't you ever do that again, Peter!' the woman's voice faded with the slamming of the car doors. Old Red heard the engine roar to life and he listened to the vehicle sounds until they were lost even to his keen ears. He rested his head more comfortably on his forepaws and gave a great sigh, his golden-tawny eyes half closing as he dozed again in the heat of the day. The cock stonechat had ceased its calling and flown down to drink from a tiny pool deep-hidden amongst the gorse where bee sounds lulled the fox to sleep.

The sun blazed into the quarry as it moved across the afternoon sky, the great orb of fire sending a ray of fierce light to penetrate through a shard of broken bottle glass resting on the quarry floor. The glass caught and held the sunbeam, directing it as a ray of white-hot heat pinpointing upon tinder-dry gorse stems. A tiny circle of black appeared at the end of the light beam burning its way into the shrivelled gorse plant. A puff of blue smoke suddenly rose into the air spiralling upwards into the still-ness. The pinpoint of black turned red, glowing then sparking brightly as the relentless sunbeam continued to burn into the heartwood. Suddenly, with a sound like that of an adder striking, the branch caught fire, hissing and crackling, a trickle of flame running hungrily along its length, leaping from left to right as it sought further fuel.

High overhead a buzzard's keen eyes saw the smoke and sudden burst of flame and he cried aloud the mewing cry of all buzzards, circling lower to suddenly veer away as more smoke billowed from the bushes overgrowing the quarry entrance.

Old Red heard the hawk's cry and half opening his eyes, gazed into the tangle of gorse stems before him. Yawning widely, his eyes saw many swallows, swifts and martins swooping and wheeling against the blue sky and then they were suddenly lost from view. He stared hard at billowing smoke clouds then started to his feet as a loud crackling sound alarmed him. All sleep left him now as an acrid scent assailed his nos-trils and eyes, causing them to smart and water. He ran forward then halted, snarling in fear and anger as he found himself faced by a wall of fire, which snarled and spat more fiercely than he, and he cowered back. All around him bracken, gorse and slender saplings were ablaze, smoke rushing skywards, as more undergrowth became engulfed by flames. Sparks hit the fox's coat and burnt his nose causing him to snap and snarl in anger. Fear tightened his belly into a knot and he ran about the quarry in a frenzy, his eyes never leaving the advancing flames which roared now as if in a fury at being roused on this lazy summer afternoon.

A stoat ran across Old Red's path chattering in fear and snapping at the fox in desperation as the larger animal trampled unwittingly upon it in his own haste and panic. Birds flew into the quarry-clearing to fly straight up over its face, some almost blinded by the smoke, which drove them from broods already consumed by flames. The 'chak, chak, seee-chak!' calls of the stonechats sounded above the flames as the two adults flew about the gorse tops, perching and calling into the smoke until the flames drove them back and they could no longer see their nest or even where it had been in the cloud of blue grey enveloping all in its path. The female stonechat called once more to her mate and they flew up and over the quarry top.

A rabbit screamed in agony as fire-scorched earth burnt its running feet until it was deep below ground in burrows of welcoming coolness which the flames could not reach, huddling in the darkness with others of its kind. Above ground a red deer hind, parted from her small group, crashed blindly out of the pall of smoke and flames eating their steady way across the quarry floor, the deer's eyes rolling in terror, her hooves flashing at Old Red's head in her fear, missing him as the fox swung away to run again at the quarry face.

Again he saw the stoat rearing up before him to leap lithely on to a ledge of slate, scrabbling at loose stones to fall back helplessly. Again the little mustela tried, nearer the fire now, and the fox ran after it, leaping high, scrabbling with his forepaws and hind legs working frenziedly together, the sharp stone cutting his pads until they bled as he dragged himself painfully upwards with bursting smoke-filled lungs. Another ledge was before him and a crashing blow from the hooves of the deer drove the breath from Old Red as she leapt over his body to reach safer ground. With pain-filled eyes the fox saw the deer leap agilely along the ledge into more smoke clouds and then the stoat passed him to be lost in the blueness and stench. He was alone with the fire. Old Red's legs shook and he almost fell back into the flame-filled quarry. He looked behind him but there was naught but the terrible flames and heat. He glanced down to see tongues of flame lick and swallow the last of the bracken in the quarry as a wall of flames leapt along an up-draught, roaring angrily along the ledge, as long-dead leaves and twigs eagerly fed them.

Old Red felt a searing pain at his flanks. He yelped aloud, turning in fury upon this unknown adversary that he could find no way to fight. The flames licked higher, shrivelling black the red campions growing over the quarry top, as Old Red moved further along the ledge. At last, finding cool earth beneath his feet he leapt blindly into swirling smoke to find himself on green grass surrounded by trees.

The fox had climbed to the very top of the quarry and found himself amongst a stand of hazel growing from ground too rocky for afforestation close to a plantation of larches, and he ran with aching lungs into the green-ness. Though his whole body hurt he did not pause in his headlong dash through the young trees, nor did he feel the whipping of unbrashed branches upon his face until the sounds of the raging fire were no more within his ears and head. As he ran he heard the wail of a siren in the distance, but he knew not what it was nor that a woman who lived in a cottage nearby had informed others about the fire.

Old Red passed the red deer hind who was standing quietly with her calf in the shade of alder trees where she had left it earlier in the day, then he felt water beneath his feet, its coolness welcoming, and stopped running to drink deeply from it. The deer moved beside him to drink as peace spread through them with the coldness of the water, the three red animals already forgetting the fire yet having learned well of its terrible nature.

His thirst quenched for the moment, Old Red lifted his head, breathing easier now, and leaving the deer's side he moved away in the direction he knew his home valley lay.

He felt pain in his flank again and limped, his step faltering momentarily then picking up again as he moved steadily onward amongst meadow brown and gatekeeper butterflies. He was tired. His tongue lolled as he loped along the left bank of Bradiford Water, putting up a mallard from rushes growing in a green fringe between a line of seven oaks. At the end of the trees was a small weir which he crossed, his feet splashing in the shallows where water ran smooth and blackly shining over the curved stone of the fall.

It was late afternoon as he leapt from the weir top to follow the waterway to a small island and then three more, each bearing a single oak tree where, on the last, stood a lone grey heron dozing after a meal of brown trout, head and neck sunk into its grey hunched shoulders. Old Red in his haste to reach Tutshill Woods brushed against the legs of the dozing bird who, feeling the fox and spying sudden movement through barely open pale eyes, 'kraaarked' harshly, launching itself into the branches forming a canopy immediately above it. Screaming angrily at this loss of dignity the great grey bird dropped back on green spindly legs and seeing it was only a fox disappearing in the distance, settled its old head once more into its shoulders and dreamed of a river constant with slowly moving fish.

The fox, hearing the heron's cry, increased his pace to run through an orchard where an abundance of green apples promised a heavy crop. He came to a narrow stream alight with fluttering green damselflies and almost hidden beneath rank vegetation, then a small hunting gate, rickety and leaning, upon which a robin sang its song every day. Then he ran through a spinney of scrub oak and hawthorn, leaving his footprints in the always marshy soil as Tutshill Woods loomed before him and he was home.

Old Red trotted up over the steep hill slope to the sound of willow warblers and chiffchaffs beneath trees that had known foxes for hundreds of years, following a path between their ancient trunks. Movement nearby caused him to flinch and snarl for his nerves were still fire-tense. A grey-brown-barred bird crouched defiantly over a wood pigeon which it was plucking at a favourite feeding post, and Old Red passed by the female sparrowhawk who lived in the adjoining copse. The hawk bristled angrily, fluffing her feathers, her needle-sharp talons gripping her prey fiercely but the fox moved on. The hawk did not watch him go, her mind already returning to her prey surrounded by a circle of grey feathers, and as she ate, Old Red was already lying in his earth, the green of the trees and the familiar sounds of birdsong swiftly driving the terror of the day from his mind.

Of Water Voles and Grass Snakes

•◆•

More hot, dry summer days and clear starry nights passed and Old Red enjoyed them, eating well, his coat shining red, showing his fine condition. On one hot August day he was lying peacefully in bracken watching two kingfishers darting along the stream to the weir pool where they caught small fish, taking them upstream to a circular hole amongst the gnarled roots of a waterside tree. Here the kingfishers had their nest and were busily raising four young of a second brood for the year, the nestlings beginning to approach the entrance to the tunnel that had been the only home they knew. Soon they would be flying free like their parents to eventually discover home territories for themselves somewhere in the North Devon countryside.

Old Red's interest had been held by the colourful chestnut, blue and white birds, as they passed and re-passed his hiding place close to the cooling water of the stream. His earth was hot under the afternoon sun but here it was cooler, the green canopy of oak and ash with underlying hazel and holly providing a secluded lair.

He had lain thus for much of the day, occasionally dozing, when human voices once more carried to his keen ears, the fox looking towards Playford Mill, now a whitewashed house amongst trees across the field on another part of the waterway. He did not move other than to raise his head to see a man, woman and two children strolling slowly in the sunshine.

The man sat himself on the stream bank in high grass, watching his wife and children kneeling to examine wildflowers as they enjoyed the sights and sounds of the countryside.

'Listen, can you hear the gorse pods popping?' the woman asked her son and daughter, and they listened to the loud cracking as gorse seeds scattered widely over the sun-baked ground along with dozens of little grey gorse weevils released from their plant prisons where they had been since the spring. A golden-ringed dragonfly zoomed low over the water-side herbage flying close to the water surface in leisurely fashion to where others of its kind were hanging from ferns on the sunny side of the stream. The insect's large, green compound eyes saw the family of humans as it passed them by, then turned as it encountered another male patrolling its own stretch of water.

'Gosh, look at that,' said the little girl as they all watched the insect swerve to turn back along its route. 'What a lovely dragonfly.' They watched it chase a bumble bee until the two insects were gone from sight where the weir pool showed the beginning of the mill leat, hidden beneath a swathe of pink Himalayan balsam that slowly spread year by year towards the village.

The girl pointed to Herb-robert and field stitchwort, excited at her own knowledge of the wildflowers as her brother went to sit by his father to watch the water for fish.

Old Red watched them for a while, the two kingfishers having gone from view beyond where a clump of hemlock water-dropwort greenly curtained a bend in the stream. Becoming restless he yawned widely and rose, shaking himself on tensed legs then wandering off along the leat path. No one saw him as he slipped silently beneath the alder trees, a tawny shadow now as he moved through the dense stand of balsam, the seed pods of which curled then flicked their seeds far and wide with his passing. Arriving at the weir which divided the main stream from the leat, Old Red splashed into the shallows, holding his face up into the weir waterfall, allowing the fresh water to pour over him as he drank, joyously revelling in the coolness and in his own health and vigour. He stood thus for brief moments then swam twice around the weir pool, splashing up on to the bank then downstream in the water until he arrived at a larger pool where dippers nested within the cavern of a leaning oak tree's roots. Here he left the water, shaking his coat, then lay in a sunlit glade amongst the many flowering grasses.

With the hot sun drying his coat he dozed quietly until the harsh cries of many gulls attracted his attention skywards where the large white birds circled and dipped with hundreds of swallows and martins. Wheeling and diving, their white bodies flashing in the sunlight, the gulls were feasting on thousands of winged ants. The insects had awaited this moment to erupt from their many nests in nuptial flight, mating on the wing, to be taken by the birds or fall back to earth, the males to die, the larger queens to tear off their wings and seek out a site in which to over-winter and lay fertile eggs, probably for several years as a result of the one mating. And even as Old Red watched, hundreds more of the tiny meadow ants poured from a nest beside him, some climbing into his fur until, irritated, he rose and splashed once more into the stream, ridding himself of them as he crossed into the water meadow to trot back towards the woods.

He loped through a field of cattle, neither taking interest in the other, and leaping the leat which was wide and deep here beneath elder trees, he paused, seeing a spray of ripe blackberries. Carefully, he ate them, taking each from the end of its stem delicately so as to avoid the sharp thorns. He enjoyed the moist sweetness of the fruit then drank briefly to wander sniffing along the bank, learning of the passing of others, his paws imprinting the soft mud, his tracks joining those of a moorhen, which had earlier passed that way. Movement across the leat caught his eye and Old Red froze in his tracks, immediately becoming part of the greens and browns of the leat vegetation as he dropped to his belly.

The movement continued, rushes at the water's edge waving, and then into view came a water vole its brown fur shaggy in appearance, to sit hunched amongst the high grass to take hold of and begin chewing at a succulent stem.

Arvic was in his third summer, a good age for a water vole. He lived here in tunnels with entrances above and below the water level where he was relatively safe from his main predators, the mink, stoats and weasels of the valley. Only once had he come very close to death, when a grey heron had tried to eat him during the previous winter, the heron's usually swift downward stab weakened by its own hunger, allowing Arvic to escape into his tunnelled home. A mink had once attempted to take him but Arvic had remained within the entrance to his lair, snapping each time the mink's fierce head had closed on the tunnel entrance, the mink moving away to seek less wary, prey.

Now he munched on the juicy stem of vegetation, enjoying the warmth of the sun, his keen ears listening for unwelcome sounds.

Old Red watched the water vole feeding. He had seen Arvic and his kind many times along the waterways but they were not his chosen prey and he moved away into sallow bushes and up over the hill slope below the wood. The water vole, hearing the fox nearby ceased feeding, remaining still, his bright eyes searching the banks but seeing nothing untoward he continued feeding, happily unaware of the fox's comings and goings.

Old Red passed beneath gorse bushes watched by a female linnet carrying food for a late brood of young, now almost fully fledged. He brushed under loose wires, which served to keep cattle out of the wood, walking along the lower path where much holly grew. Voices told him that the humans were still by the stream so he moved deeper into the trees away from them to a spring, about which grew male and hart's-tongue ferns. He drank deeply from the cold water, refreshing himself, lingering in the coolness of this the greenest part of the wood.

He stepped forward then drew back sharply as a foul smell struck his nostrils and something beneath his feet moved to one side. Old Red stared, head on one side, as a large grass snake drew itself up, raising the forepart of its body into an S-shaped loop. Expelling air with an explosive hiss, it lunged forward with its head, feinting a strike with jaws closed, not making contact with the fox who swiftly withdrew to dash in again, striking the snake a glancing blow with one forepaw. The snake raised again flicking its tongue nervously in and out between closed jaws to then fall forward, rolling over on to its back with jaws now wide open, lying quite still with its tongue protruding. Old Red stared at the snake warily but it did not move. He stepped forward and placed a tentative paw upon it but there was no movement.

Losing interest, Old Red turned, trotting away up the hillside towards his earth, his feet cool upon the mosses and yellow cow wheat which grew abundantly amongst the trees, its flowers always facing the sun. Behind him Natrix the grass snake moved, gliding silently away into the undergrowth, no longer feigning death in the manner of his kind now that the fox had gone.

Along the River Yeo

❖

Ona day when the hot sun lowered into a bank of pale mist rolling inland from the sea coast, Old Red ventured into the fading daylight of an early September evening.

After drinking from the shallows of the stream where it curled gleaming away from the weir, the fox sat with the woods behind him, preening his soft fur with little nibbling strokes of his fangs, combing the white chest hairs painstakingly, at ease in the peace of the valley farmland.

A pale grey and white bird flew out from its perch on an alder tree surrounded by brambles bearing the ripe glistening fruit of early autumn. The spotted flycatcher caught an insect in flight, flying back to its perch, building up its fat reserves as were the swallows, swifts and other summer migrants, all feeling the stimulus to follow the sun.

Everywhere the haws along the hedgerows were a million crimson pinpoints of light, with here and there the bright scarlet hips of dog rose. The flycatcher appeared again as Old Red shook himself before moving off to follow the stream, the bird following a curving aerial route out over the brambles and back to its alder branch, catching insects with each short flight in this, its last month in the valley. Soon the vast journey to its wintering quarters across the ocean would begin.

Old Red pounced, catching a field vole which he ate on the move, leaping and pirouetting with the sheer joy of living, drinking again briefly at Shearford Bridge, sneezing water from his nostrils where he probed too deeply as he drank, seeing the long shape of a salmon move slowly upstream, the first to penetrate these waters on the autumn run.

The fox walked through a gateway by a stone bridge bright with golden and pale green lichens, jumping the always muddy patch here near rusting sluice machinery where once had been a small weir. Shadowy brown trout darted swiftly before him as his own shadow fell on the water surface, the fish hiding beneath the bridge arch as he passed by. A dark brown bird with flashing white breast flew low above the water, landing beyond him to dip and bob on a shining stone in midstream upon which showed the chalky white droppings of the bird's previous visits. The dipper turned a complete bobbing circle as Old Red approached to pass its perch, the bird's plumage merging with the water splashes, and then it flew upstream calling shrilly above the water sounds.

Old Red ran at a lone rabbit which stood alertly amongst buttercups, its long ears gloeing red where the light from the setting sun shone through, but the fox had run on too early, the rabbit easily reaching the dense brambly hedge bank where, with a flick of its white scut it vanished into the greenery. The fox trotted back to where the stream flowed beneath ash trees, then widened out into a deep pool where the gnarled and twisted roots of ancient hawthorns formed the old holt of otters.

He sniffed at the taint of a dog as a wren scolded him from its safe perch amongst ivy climbing a waterside oak, then he leapt the hedge bank to avoid soft mud at a place where two fields joined and a mass of barbed wire strands prevented cattle and old people from following this route. A little owl flew from a favourite branch to dip low over Old Red's head, telling the fox it was his territory, then flying higher on its soft rounded wings the owl perched where it could watch for beetles and moths in the twilight.

On the fox trotted to a stand of trees where the stream rushed over stones in a torrent of white water, pausing as he heard muffled voices coming from above him where the gardens of many houses lay in a neat row along the field top. He moved on, keeping below the fence line, snarling at the crackling bonfire which belched smoke in the garden of one house, remembering fire and the smell of burning. And then he was at Bradiford Bridge where the mist was thicker, replacing the smoke, smelling of the sea and the river from whence it had blown on a stiffening breeze, its pale wraiths already filling the bridge arch where a pair of mallard dozed close together.

Old Red ran up the bank where one wall of the bridge adjoined a small clump of planted conifers, to run along the road, quiet now in the mist-filled evening save for the murmur of voices and laughter issuing from the lounge bar of an inn. He was seen by a young couple, gazing dreamily from the windows, arms about each other's black, leather-jacketed shoulders as they sipped pale amber liquid from fine-stemmed glasses. They gazed after the fox then at each other, enjoying the sight, saying nothing as the strains of Waylon Jennings going back to 'Luchenback Texas' followed the fox along the road.

The fox trotted on, passing a high grass verge where a longstone menhir had been placed upright at the junction of two roads, and then into Pilton Pathfields, once the home of many hundreds of frogs and toads in a marshy reedbed until a school and houses took away their homes. He passed a garage forecourt where an attendant stared in amazement at the fox appearing out of the mist, pouring petrol on to his own shoes and those of his customer as the car tank he was filling overflowed.

Old Red entered an alleyway between brick walls, unaware of the stir caused by his passing, to come to the banks of the River Yeo meandering about the wide curving banks of a park. Seven mute swans swam lazily where the mist curled gently over the river, creeping along the wooden planking retaining walls heavy with green moss cushions and the slime left by an ebbing tide, the old timbers rotting now, long-neglected and fungi-ridden.

Old Red climbed down the steep bank where he saw movement near the water's edge amongst dead hogweed stalks standing starkly brittle from dank soil. He watched a mink swim out from the bank and across the river where it clambered easily, rippling amongst the tall vegetation as a black, sinewy, snake-like creature, to disappear into the park amongst horse chestnut trees heavily laden with spiked conker fruit. Old Red raised his head, nostrils sniffing the air, but now only the water moved below him. He trotted up over the bank to walk amongst timber stacks, which reached high to a huge shed rooftop and black shadows. The great shed was without a wall where it joined the river bank and it was here, close to the water's edge, that the fox came upon a large dead fish lying upon a mudflat laid bare by the ebbing tide an hour before. The fish was a tope, one of the smooth dogfish family, and would not have been here but for a sea angler who lived nearby tossing it as an unwanted catch over the causeway wall. The fish had splashed amongst black-headed gulls swimming on the water with several mallard, causing commotion amongst them, some tearing flesh from it even as it sank and rolled with the ebb current to come to rest on the mud ledge where Old Red now ate from it hungrily.

A few people passed over the causeway on their way to or from the town, none glancing over to see the fox enjoying his meal. He ate his fill where he was, knowing how far from his home he had come and not wishing to carry prey back to his earth. He nosed at the river water but did not drink, for the surface stank and there was the hue of rainbows upon it. He left the river bank to trot back along the footpath route, finding his own scent line, which he followed past the now darkened garage and along the Abbey road to Bradiford.

Here at the village bottom he crossed the stone bridge, not following his former route along the stream, and entered Halls Mill Lane. Half-way along it he heard shuffling sounds in the darkness and the scent of pheasant came clearly to him. He slowed by the leat where the heady smell of dying Himalayan balsam was strong and could just see the large game bird before him at the lane edge. He rushed at the bird, expecting flight or some resistance but there was none, the bird dying just before he reached it. Old Red sniffed it puzzled, but the smell of the bird was fresh and the fox fastened his jaws upon it at the neck, trotting with it, dragging it into the mill field, his eyes straining into the now thick mist as he used the hedge banks to find his way homeward. Once back at his earth he laid himself down with his prey, pleased with his night's hunting, not knowing the pheasant had died from gunshot wounds taken earlier that evening as it flew over Periwinkle Wood and, wounded, had flapped and glided its way to Halls Mill Lane where, striking power lines hidden by the mist, it had dropped unconscious to the lane.

Old Red slept as a light wind blew over the hills from Exmoor, the fox dreaming of lush wooded valleys filled with pheasants, rabbits and clear-water streams.

Of Autumn, Little Boys
and Wigeon

•◆•

There are many facets to the woodland scene and when hushed voices fell on to the ears of Old Red one quiet evening he stirred uneasily from his lair to gaze about him into the trees.

The year was getting old, fully ripened blackberries hung like dark jewels catching the setting sun's last glints, swaying slightly in the gentlest of breezes. Old Red leaned forward, stretching his neck to reach and take one of the fruits, eating it as he watched for movement amongst the trees.

The murmur came again but no nearer and Old Red knew that humans were by the stream at the bottom of the wood. He made his way between the ancient beech and oak trees, his curiosity aroused, his dark shadowy form hidden and silent as he moved swiftly to where he knew he could better observe the source of the sounds.

Pausing as he neared the stream, the fox crouched in the confines of a large holly tree, which spread its branches around him, hiding him from all watchers. Head on one side he watched movement close by the gnarled beech tree at the entrance to the woods. Hidden behind the beech, the oldest tree in the wood, two boys gazed intently into the area of red light cast by a torch, upon the glass of which they had stuck transparent red toffee paper. They carefully moved the beam from side to side, the light showing the trees and surrounding bushes, the ferns and grasses lit with an eerie glow as moths, turned pink by the light fluttered along its beam to fly on into the woodland night.

Then, as if in answer to schoolboy prayers, a tawny owl floated majestically into the beam and was followed by it until lost from sight amongst the trees, its plumply feathered body reflecting pink and dreamlike in the glow from the torchlight.

Old Red continued to watch from his hiding place as the boys chattered in excited whispers watching the owl fly by. A rustling of leaves and snuffling sounds came loud to all the listening ears. The torch beam moved to trap the sound and into view came a hedgehog, staring short-sightedly about, sniffing the air as it came. Its nose burrowed into the leaf litter and with audible crunching another small creature ended its days as hedgehog food.

The two boys watched silently all the while, marvelling at the sights and sounds of nature, happy they had read somewhere about red torchlight not disturbing wild creatures.

Old Red, bored with the scene, knowing instinctively that no danger threatened, rose and trotted from concealment, silently loping along the path before them. The two youngsters saw him simultaneously, the one holding the torch aiming it at the fox with a hand that trembled with excitement as, gripping his companion's arm with his free hand, he could only croak, 'a fox', with a throat suddenly gone dry.

His friend did not answer. With open mouths they watched Old Red pass them by to slip soundlessly through the gap between post and railing at the wood entrance. He vanished in the gloom beyond the torch beam and was gone. Beneath the giant beech tree the two boys still gazed, in awe of all they had seen in their short time within the woods.

'Gosh, nobody will believe us,' whispered the torch carrier. 'Our first night trip and we've seen owls, foxes, hedgehogs and millions of moths already,' he said in the exaggerated way of the young, like many of his age apt to pluralise the good things in life.

'Yep, millions,' agreed his friend, already filled with favourite memories to savour to the full in his own time, and drawings he would do at home on rainy days.

In their notebooks at home, however, every correct detail would be recorded, with sketches neatly drawn for comparison with sightings on other days and nights.

Old Red had already cast the voices from his mind and was a mile away, passing the old stone archway of a folly on a hillside overlooking the main road between towns and villages. A long-eared bat dropped from the ivy covering the stone wall and flew low past his head to begin its nightly hunt for insects along the Bradiford Water and lane. This was Plecotus of the yellow-brown fur and pale face, his long ears almost three-quarters of his body length. He lived the summer here at Triumphal Arch, the name given to the folly by locals, and at ten years old was past the age of breeding, having outlived many of his colony born the same year. All summer he dined well on a diet of noctuid moths and other insects, many taken from the tree foliage whilst others were caught in full flight.

Each night Plecotus groomed his fur carefully as the sun set, then flew and hunted Poleshill Lane on and off during the night-time, the dawn rising of the sun always finding him back at his daytime roost.

Plecotus was old and wily and had avoided for years his only enemies, owls and the wild farm cats from the valley farms below his home. As the bat flew on its nightly jaunt, Old Red was rapidly covering the ground to the main road where he paused by a gateway as the glaring and blaring of passing vehicles lit up the hedgerow, throwing leaves, dust and fumes into his eyes and nose. During a lull in the traffic he ran across the tarmac to a central grass verge and then more tarmac to the safety of a high hedgerow.

Here he entered a field, pushing beneath a five-barred gate as the sounds of the estuary night came fully to his ears. A light breeze from the river carried the first real fall of autumn leaves spinning to the ground, a few falling into the Bradiford Water which here was ending its journey, spilling out under a disused railway bridge into the tidal waters of the River Taw.

The calls of oystercatchers and curlew were loud upon the air as Old Red paused to sniff the breeze at a meander in the stream where earlier an otter had left a spraint to tell others of its kind that it was about. A gibbous moon turned the waters of the river silver with its light, rushes, reeds and nettles silhouetted black against the rippling brightness which stretched as far as the eye could see in both directions. It was close to this spot that Old Red had come on the stormy night that had first brought him from his birthplace to Tutshill, though what memory of that night remained in Old Red's mind is known only to foxes.

The deep-bellied chugging of a sand barge mingled with the calls of birds as the vessel loomed into the night, lights shining from its black shape, their reflections rocking brightly on the wash cast by its passing as the barge made its way with its heavy load of sand and gravel to the quay on the River Yeo.

A flight of duck came off the water in front of the vessel and the wigeon whistled their 'whee-oo' calls as they rose straight out of the estuary together, a flock of some two hundred birds which had arrived but two days before. The company of wigeon wheeled in tightly flocked formation as they flew in rapid flight to find a roosting place away from the barge wake.

The duck had swum from Penhill Point and the stony ridge of Fremington beach where they had been resting during the day. With the drakes still whistling, the birds turned again to fly low over the water and spread out along the salt marshes a hundred yards from the watching fox.

These wigeon were the first to arrive back on the Taw for the winter and had flown from Iceland. Soon now their numbers would build up, other birds coming from eastern and northern Europe to feed and shelter on the inter-tidal area of the Taw and Torridge rivers which affords them shelter and food until the spring.

Old Red was now running swiftly behind a bank where grew hawthorn trees. Obscured thus from view he sped across the field where, without faltering, he dashed up and over the bank and on to the marshes. A harsh almost growling 'kraak-kraak' sounded from the nearest female wigeon, a plump bird, which rose in time with the others, only to be brought down by the charging dog fox.

Veering towards the safety of the estuary waters, the wigeon, as if drawn by a magnet, formed a dark cloud of beautiful flight that Old Red failed to see. He was already trotting back the way he had come, the duck held firmly in strong jaws watering in anticipation of the fine meal he would soon be enjoying in the safety of his snug earth.

Of Floods

•◆•

Just two days after Old Red had caught and eaten wigeon, the valley was still; not the slightest of breezes stirred the remaining leaves of the ash tree beneath which he lay on his side in the lengthening shadows creeping towards him from the west. The fox was waiting quietly for the time he knew rabbits would emerge in the field below Westaway Farm where hunting was always good at this time.

He lay watching the sky towards the west where a strange greenish light was turning the valley eerily hazy. Old Red's ears pricked forward, his eyes intent upon the scene before him for he could now hear distant rumblings from where the sun lay like a fireball on the horizon. Then they came again much louder, the darkening sky suddenly blazing with blue light as sheet lightning threw the leaves and grasses before his face into sharp silhouette. Immediately upon the flash of light came the deafening roar of thunder and Old Red bolted into the woods to hide in the quarry near the ancient beech tree. He crept beneath a ledge of rock overhang, scattering woodlice which were trundling into darker recesses feeling the storm to come, the fox crouching as rain suddenly swept in a fury of water on to the trees above his head. More lightning hit the path, dancing along the wires of the rickety fence and again came the roar of thunder as the fox tried desperately to hug the very earth with his frightened frame. Rain, violently thrown from clouds as black as the moles which lived in the valley, broke through the autumn canopy to lash the land, turning the pathway into a stream as it fell. In moments the small cave where Old Red lay was curtained by a sheet of water, as the fox looked out at the world of strange water shapes, lit by occasional blue flashes. Old Red remained dry. His hurried retreat had taken him to safety as it had done several times before in his life and he lay listening to the wild sounds about him.

The storm sweeping in from the estuary was at its height as it passed over the valley, beating against the hills as it hurled its rains at Exmoor. Cattle from the fields had stampeded, a small herd of Friesians galloping up over the mud-strewn slopes to the farm at Westawa. One cow taking fright as lightning bounced from the galvanised roof of a shed, galloping on through the farm, churning the lawns and flower-beds before the farmhouse, and on to the main road. Startled vehicle drivers, seeing the black and white apparition through rain-swept windscreens, frantically braked, causing more chaos as the terrified animal ran amongst them.

An oak tree fell high in the woods as lightning ripped into its roots, the tree spilling two grey squirrels from their drey built close in against its trunk. The two soaked animals ran along sodden branches to follow each other into a drey in the next tree where they huddled together with eyes closed to wait out the storm.

The water of the stream and leat rose sharply, spilling over into the meadows. Stone loaches already brought to the surface by the lack of oxygen caused by the thundery conditions, dashed wildly about as they found themselves cast into the swiftly flooding fields along with small trout and minnows.

The sun had dipped beneath the horizon, the only light now that of the lightning flashes which momentarily lit the valley. For two hours Old Red remained within the safe confines of his quarry-face hideout. With the passing rumbles of the storm came a new sound to his ears, the soft flight calls of incoming redwings intermixed with the sharper, louder notes of fieldfares following the weather inland along the migratory routes afforded by the river valleys. The thrushes had flown the hundreds of miles by night from Scandinavia, nocturnal migrants winging in on the very slipstream of the storm and now they would feed along the valleys and hillsides until March beckoned them northwards back to their breeding haunts.

Old Red rose. Water that had cascaded before him from the ledge above his cave now fell as a steady drip and he knew the rain had ceased. He stretched, yawning widely, and stepped out into the night his paws slithering on earth, which had become slippery mud mere seconds after the storm had broken.

Needing to eat he splashed out of the wood into the valley now bathed in pale moonlight, a valley he did not recognise. Standing under the two oak trees by a stile leading into the woods, he stared out over a vast lake upon which a silver moon floated on gently rippling water. Far to the north-east Old Red heard the last rumblings of thunder but before him all was still, only the flooded fields and fallen trees telling of its passing. A ripple near a clump of forlorn looking nettles and balsam became Arvic the water vole who left the water to clamber on to the high ground, his arrival causing the fox to see three rabbits, muddied and bedraggled, huddled against the nearby tree roots. Old Red, sniffing at them when they did not move, found they had drowned but he did not take the limp, soaking carcasses even though he had eaten carrion before in his life.

Old Red turned back into the woods. He did not relish hunting over flooded terrain as yet unexplored. On reaching the main path he came upon a mink about to eat its rabbit kill taken beside the stream moments before as the animal crouched beside its flooded burrow. Here the mink had found it as she wandered from her lair, as much at home in water as on land as she hunted the stream banks. The rabbit, a large doe, had put up a token resistance, digging her powerful hind legs into the mink's stomach as she felt her assailant's teeth fasten at her throat, and then she had died, seeing the head of the fox loom over them, then nothing more.

The mink turned, snarling as she sensed the fox's presence and fell back a spitting fury, her one error, for Old Red, as quick almost as the lightning, snapped the rabbit into his jaws and bolted along the path, his long legs taking the steep upward slope far too quickly for any mink to follow. The mink stared after him in the darkness but the fox was gone amongst the trees he knew so well. Turning away the dark mustela began to hunt again along the water's edge as Old Red slipped noiselessly into his main earth, which he found was dry despite the rains. Dropping the rabbit in one corner he curled himself snugly beside it to sleep into the day.

Foxes All

⬩◆⬩

The flooded fields of the valley held water for more than a week, during which time Old Red hunted above the woods where the high ground was drier. The fox fed well on rats and voles, many of which had fled the flood areas to seek shelter in and about the woods, some becoming the easy prey of foxes and owls.

It was a late afternoon that found him leaving the spinney near Blakewell to the sound of silvery autumnal robin song issuing from hawthorn that grew beside a narrow hunting gate leading into arable fields. Three wood pigeons clattered away from where they had been eating clover, flying noisily into the safe confines of the hedgerow trees. A jay called harshly as he passed beneath its resting place and he jumped, startled by the banging of a new bird-scarer recently installed by the farmer sowing winter seed in the area. Four rooks were feeding on the carcass of a hare, its head and forelegs gone, eaten by another fox who had hunted through here on the previous night. On the distant hillside a scarlet tractor moved down over a sloping field, leaving a rich brown wake behind it as it wheeled in a wide arc to be lost behind trees at the valley bottom. A flock of starlings put up from the field, whirling like a gigantic swarm of bees, a huge wave rolling over the fields in precision flight to seek their night roost in the reed beds by the river. Old Red watched them out of sight hearing the whirring of their wings hush to silence in their passing.

Over the sloping hillside, which curled greenly towards Muddiford, two kestrels hunted, hovering together then rising high to dip then hover again, heads into the breeze that blew from the north-west. Old Red paused by a stile built across a public footpath linking two fields, as with much crawing, a flock of rooks flew up from the valley bottom to harass the birds of prey. Immediately the male kestrel, its grey head showing clearly against chestnut back and wings, called 'kee-kee-keee' and side-slipping swept away to be followed into the adjoining field by the rooks. His mate hunted on in peace, knowing well this trick they often played to draw harassing crows and rooks away from their hunting area. Old Red watched the female falcon drop to the ground to rise with a field mouse, taking it to a post where she began to tear at it with her powerful hooked bill, holding the prey clenched tightly in her talons. As the fox moved on along the valley the male kestrel reappeared above him in his hovering flight, calling a long drawn out 'kee-keee-kee' to tell his mate all was well. Old Red paused again behind a stand of foxgloves, his hackles rising as two other foxes appeared from a clump of oaks on the side of the hill a hundred fox-paces from where he stood.

The two, a vixen and a dog fox, cavorted about in the lush grass and late buttercups, leaping at each other in play. Old Red watched them. The vixen was a pale tawny red with a sandy band of fur about her middle. The locals in the nearby village had nicknamed her 'the saddle-back' for she was well known, having eluded the Hunt on a number of occasions.

Old Red wanted her. He watched her for some while as the two foxes played together, then ran lightly down over the fields towards the pair, a challenging barking growl issuing from his throat. The two foxes paused in their play, the vixen withdrawing a short distance to sit and watch as the dog foxes faced each other, each trying to out-stare his rival.

A low growl came from the throat of the older dog fox as Old Red circled him warily then rushed in to find his adversary had leapt sideways, avoiding him with ease. They chased in wide circles on the hillside, occasionally one or the other making sudden rushes with little contact.

The sun dipped behind the westward hills sending tree shadows across the field to seek out the vixen, enveloping her in their darkness. She heard a sound, turning quickly to find another dog fox, larger than both her suitors, who still chased each other on the hillside, and darker in colour than they. He nosed towards her silently, the vixen liking his scent as she made deep-throated noises to him. They ran off along the hillside together, leaping a ditch to disappear into the spinney beyond.

Seeing movement Old Red stopped in his tracks, nosing the wind. He knew the vixen had gone and still panting from the chase turned away towards Tutshill casting not a further glance in the direction of the other dog fox who stared after his departing shadow then turned to follow rabbit scent along the hedge bank. Old Red loped homeward in the owl light to hunt better-known territory, the incident forgotten. Already he could feel the chill of autumn frost in the air, the breeze cold upon his body heralding the end of summer weather, telling of the long winter months ahead.

Of Weasels

On a day when the October sun was setting on the horizon, poised redly, sending its colour across a sky with little cloud, a green woodpecker called a last laughing cry to the disappearing day. The bird flew from the bottom of Shearford Lane to the wood edge where the leaves still hanging on the trees caught the sun colour, turning from copper to purple in the swiftly fading light of the winter afternoon.

The scarlet hips of dog roses glowed in profusion along the hedgerows, shining as myriad spots of warm colour against a sepia background of twigs and branches.

From the depths of the wood came again the mocking yaffle of the woodpecker, the weird sound banshee-like in the darkening valley. Crouched against a bank where dead bracken the colour of foxes hid his shape, Old Red was eyeing a group of rabbits feeding quietly across the stream from where he hid, weighing his chances of crossing the water unseen to catch the nearest. Deciding to find a better vantage point from which to run at the group, he crouched low and stealthily made his way to where a bridge with a double gateway led to the rabbit field.

A lone partridge broke cover before him, Old Red leaping after it with a reaction born partly of surprise, but to no avail. The stocky little game bird flew off with a shirring of wings to live another day.

The fox loped along a grassy bank under the cover of a high hedge, the wet grasses soaking his coat as he wormed his way forward to better view the rabbits he knew were close by. As he raised himself to locate his prey the grasses immediately before him stirred. Old Red dropped to his belly, watching, as a pair of hunting weasels moved before him from a hollow in the ground made by the passing of cattle and humans over many years.

The scent of rabbits and that of weasels came to Old Red's nose, for all three hunters had placed themselves perfectly, heads into the wind to avoid detection by the wary rabbits.

Old Red watched curiously as one weasel moved directly in line toward the rabbits who still fed on, unaware of the predators. The other weasel slipped away into the high grass to one side, disappearing from view behind a long low bramble brake.

The two weasels were mother and son, and they had hunted the summer together with two other young who were some distance away watching from a thistle patch. The family still lived together in a pile of Scots pine logs, which lay at the bottom of an old orchard half a mile upstream from where they now hunted. The father of this family, had been killed by a Jack Russell terrier from a nearby cottage some weeks before in a dispute over a rabbit, caught but still alive, in a poacher's snare.

Now Old Red watched as the first weasel, the mother, raised herself to her full height, making a chattering noise before running the remaining distance twixt her and the nearest rabbit.

Within the distance of twice her own length from her chosen prey, Kine the weasel began to writhe and dance in the strange manner of her kind. Once she had killed a young buzzard hawk with bites to its belly as it foolishly caught her, flying with her some twenty feet from the ground before it died. Now she rolled and somersaulted ever closer to the rabbit who watched, transfixed by her tiny menacing presence. The rabbit's eyes rolled in terror, lifting towards the dark sky as it wailed a strange cry, which changed to a scream and then was still as Kine's bites and its own fear killed it.

A second scream rent the air and Old Red knew where the other weasels now were. He rose to seek his own prey but there were no live rabbits remaining for all had bolted at the sound of the second scream.

The fox looked about. Kine was at her kill and some distance away three young weasels were at theirs. With the feeling of hunger strong within him Old Red dashed across the grass, strong jaws snatching at Kine's kill, and on he ran dragging both prey and predator with him. For forty yards he ran thus, watched by three pairs of tiny eyes raised from their rabbit supper, then Old Red found his stolen meal lessen its drag as Kine released her hold, falling away to roll upright chattering in fury after the fox.

She watched Old Red bound on towards the woods and turning moved to where her young had resumed feeding, joining them to feast on a prize quite adequate for the four.

High in the woods Old Red ate, crouching outside his earth as a tawny owl called to its mate deeper amongst the trees.

Winter Tales: the Sheep Killer

◦◄◦

The winter woodland was alive with birds, small flocks of blue and great tits flitting amongst the now bare branches in the never-ending search for food. Bramblings from Europe had joined many chaffinches foraging along the hedgerows, now becoming empty of haws. Somewhere out of sight a nuthatch tapped away at a hazel nut, which it had secured in a crevice in the bark of an oak.

A dry spell had made hunting easier for Old Red over the past few days, many mice and voles being active at this time. Thus he had fed well, building up much needed reserves of strength to see him through the likely colder months ahead, the fox hunting often in the daylight hours to ensure a good food supply as is the habit of many creatures who usually hunt by night.

The fox was hunting below Upcott along level fields, which ran parallel with the main road and Taw estuary. The late afternoon sun shone brightly through the trees of the small woodland, no foliage on the branches now to obscure the sunlight. Red campions glowed in amongst the intense blue flowers of green alkanet standing stiffly in the hedge bottom, both wildflowers blooming late into the winter months, adding their cheery colour to the day.

Old Red entered a part of the wood where hazel grew so thickly amongst the trees he could barely see into the dense shrub layer before him as he nosed forward, every sense alert.

As he pushed under a fallen tree branch which leaned against a scrub oak, his sixth sense told him something was amiss and he paused, one forefoot raised as he stared into the green gloom beneath the trees. A low growl sounded from the depths of the vegetation and fear struck momentarily through the fox, to be replaced swiftly by an alertness and cunning that had oft-times saved his life. The growling came again, louder now, rustling movements causing the fox to turn away and run into more open woodland, to break into a gallop as he realised a chase was on. He sped through trees along a narrow overgrown footpath then veered into the fields over a hedge bank which was mere roots and soil where he ran faster hearing the sound of his pursuer following, as yet some distance behind. Old Red ran along the line of hedgerow leaping high into the hedge at the field corner to force his way through brambles and leap the ditch beyond.

Now he ran back along the other side of the same hedgerow, doubling back on its far side to outwit his pursuer, then through a gap in a broken stone wall where he followed a stream for a field length to dash into a stand of trees, then paused to look back the way he had come.

Upon the stone wall, close to the gap through which he had just run, stood a large black lurcher dog, rough of coat and as large as a labrador. It saw Old Red even as he looked and, leaping from the hedge bank into the field, it bounded over the grass with great strides and slavering mouth. Old Red turned and ran, no fear in him yet knowing the dog meant danger. He ran through another hedgerow, passing an old farm trailer being towed by a tractor on its way to dump manure in a field corner. The tractor driver watched the fox dash across the field to where a huge hollow oak leaned into Poleshill Lane next to the old stone folly, seeing the animal squeeze into a hole at its base as the large lurcher arrived and began to scratch frenziedly. Old Red ran up the tree hollow, his claws scrabbling for a hold as he reached the top to find himself peering down into the shadowy trackway of the lane. He could hear the dog snapping angrily below and he stayed where he was, safe at least for a time and unwilling to leap and run further with his foe so close. He heard a shout and running footsteps as the farm labourer approached though he could see no one, only the route of the lane below him.

More shouts and then a snapping yelp, and silence. Old Red waited. The sounds of dog and human had ceased. A hen blackbird perched near his head then flew to the ground to begin scuffing at the loose soil and leaf debris for worms and grubs. A dunnock hopped about amongst buckler and hart's-tongue ferns beneath him, its soft greys and browns blending with the herbage as it searched for tiny insects and weed seeds. The fox waited until his legs became cramped then eased himself back down inside the tree hollow. There was no movement or shadow at the hole through which he had entered. He squeezed out into the daylight, feeling the blood returning to aching limbs as he moved cautiously into the field, hearing no sounds other than the continued scuffing of the blackbird nearby.

For a moment he remained crouching, peering through tall herbage. The dog had gone. He could see the tractor and trailer standing under trees at the field corner but no sign of a human. A sudden shift in the breeze brought the scent of animal flesh to his nostrils and he turned away, mounting the hedge bank to drop lightly into Poleshill Lane where double strands of barbed wire across its route kept cattle from straying along it to the road. Here he found a dead sheep, partly eaten, in a hollow by the side of the lane where the branches of a huge sycamore tree reached out across the path forming a natural bower, which screened the dead animal from view. Old Red sniffed about the carcass, seeing where another animal had torn the throat and eaten part of its meat. It seemed fresh still and Old Red was about to tear a portion of the carrion to take back to his earth in the next valley when he heard a twig snap and he whirled to bolt away into the tree-lined lane.

The farm labourer dropped into the lane where he had seen the fox crouching over the sheep carcass, anger and curiousity flooding his thoughts. A while before, he had sent the black lurcher packing with a well-aimed clod of earth and had remained hidden behind his vehicle for the fox to emerge from its hollow-tree hiding place. He had watched him creep from the hole, admiring Old Red's litheness and cunning, unable to resist watching the animal's behaviour, and then he had quickly crept across the field until, eyes on the fox, he had stepped on the fallen dry branch of a tree and snapped it, only to see Old Red's immediate departure. Now he leaned over the dead sheep seeing the method of kill. He looked about him. Sheep wool torn from the fleece hung in a mass on the lower strand of barbed wire close by, showing where the animal had attempted to flee from whatever had killed it. He examined the soil around and about, finding sheep tracks and with them the clear imprints of a large dog.

'The black dog,' he muttered to himself, 'a rogue dog,' he said aloud, and left the lane, running to the tractor to drive off to tell his employer of the afternoon's events.

Old Red, meanwhile, had reached the field adjoining Anchor Mills, which had once been Hall's Mill, the first of seven mills along the water-way, and he drank from the stream where it ran by well-mown banks and the house. He slipped under the wooden gate to be chased by the horse that lived here, the fox not minding the large animal, which chased all who entered the field. He loped on towards Tutshill Woods, thoughts of the day gone from his mind, which was once more intent upon the hunt for food. He did not know that his chase with the dog earlier had led to the discovery of a rogue sheep killer being in the area, and that he had in an odd way helped to set in motion the full-scale hunt for his pursuer of the afternoon. The black lurcher had once been one of two owned by a local man who enjoyed a spot of poaching and lamping, but it had fought with its older companion and fled to live a life in the wild rather than return to its former home. For a while it had foraged the dustbins and bin-liners of people who on seeing it attempted to do it harm, the lurcher turning from catching rabbits and duck to killing sheep as easy targets for its food. Knowing no different, it had found lambs and sheep easy prey and filling. Now with the blow from the farm labourer's well-aimed missile it was already two miles beyond the area of its human pursuers, heading for the open countryside of Exmoor.

Old Red left Poleshill Lane out of his daytime excursions following the lurcher incident, preferring to hunt the valley near his home and beyond to the Valley of the Hunter's Moon, an area away from the town and one where fewer humans were to be found.

Of Long-eared Owls
and Chicken

◆

The icy blast of a January wind whistled against the westward edge of the woods, whipping dead leaves from the cold, dark earth to toss them against the black sodden trunks of the oak, ash and beeches in a frenzy. Save for the wind sound and the creaking of branches, the night was silent and bleak. At Yarnerwood Cottage, two fields from the wood edge, a light went out, the silvery rectangle of frosted grasses in the adjoining field disappearing with the flicking of the switch inside the little home as the last of the family to retire for the night plodded upstairs, warmed by the log fire dying in the grate.

On the hearth slept a tabby cat, his sides rising and falling, whiskers twitching in some mouse-hunting dream, whilst in the stables nearby two horses with Arab blood lay asleep in body-warmed straw.

Gliding on the wind came the dark shape of a large bird followed by another, silent and long of wing, orange eyes straining for a clearer sight of the dark mass of trees looming ahead. With incredible accuracy on such a dark and wild night, the birds allowed the howling winds to sweep them into the blackness of the trees to alight on adjacent Scots pines in its western corner. A deep 'whoo-hoo-hoooo' came from one of the birds, a sound like that made when one blows across the top of an empty bottle, and they both settled themselves against the sides of the trees away from the weather, sheltering against the rough bark.

The birds were long-eared owls from the north and like others of their kind they had moved south, driven by the unfriendly weather in their breeding areas.

Not so many years before, a pair of these owls had nested in March in Shearford Lane at a time when it was greatly overgrown and impenetrable, the female laying two white eggs on the ground beneath dense brambles. The birds had been forced to desert the eggs when the lane was cleared by ramblers requiring the walk, and none had returned since to attempt to nest there again.

They had flown far these new arrivals and they paid no attention to a new sound pervading the woodland, the clanging of church bells denoting the time of 8.30pm on a Tuesday, a time when bell-ringers practised their skills each week. The bell sound, from Pilton Church, snatched from the grey stone belfry of the ancient church tower by the gusting wind, followed the gaze of the brazen image of a cockerel on its summit to clamour its way over Ladywell, over houses old and new, deflecting off Anchor Mills to reach Tutshill Woods where it became muted by the trees.

Old Red had been sleeping soundly in a disused badgers' sett all that day, watched over by the skull of an old boar badger that had died there two years previously. The fox's ears had caught the sound of the bells upon the wind and he lifted his head to listen to the storm, his gaze fixed on the entrance hole to the sett where badgers had once toiled to build their stronghold home. All he could see was the dull grey light of a winter's night and shadowy strands of ivy which grew over the outside of the sett obscuring it from all but the sharpest eyes. The badgers had long since moved to a sett at a converted mill, now a farm, a mile or so away, only visiting the wood for an occasional exploration of old haunts, their visits often depending on wind direction and the consequent arrival of earthworms upon the hillside.

The fox was hungry, the storm having lasted for three days, the female wild duck Old Red had brought with him being now just bones and a few feathers. The wild duck, now commonly called mallard when once only the males had borne that name, had been lean enough as it was and thus Old Red needed to hunt.

He rose stiffly and shook himself, nosing out into the cold, dank woodland where drops of rainwater spattered on him as he passed under hazel shrub layer and followed the old path leading under the gnarled beech tree and out into the leat meadow. Across the meadow he padded, squeezing under an old iron railing that served as a stockproof fence in a gateway, then through a wider gateway into the accommodation road by Playford Mill. Passing uphill to Westaway Plain, he loped by a high stone wall which had once been partly demolished by a crashing aircraft during the 1940s and which still showed the repair stonework of that terrible day.

Old Red trotted by former waterworks buildings to wander down a wide pavement and grass verge by the main road, stepping where a meteorite had fallen leaving a huge crater, now long forgotten, other than by those who had lived in the area at the time of the strange event. Now the road reflected the lights of traffic on glistening tarmac, the hissing roar of passing vehicles causing his ears and tail to drop with fear.

The rain had ceased, the wind dropping as Old Red went through an open gateway marking the entrance to a footpath leading steeply down to Raleigh hamlet. Here along the cindery track he took a plump hen from outside a wire enclosure in the back garden of a cottage. His powerful jaws stilled the surprised squawk the hen had begun to utter, the bird knowing no pain or fear. He took the chicken to Roth's Mill, an old whitewashed building between Raleigh and Derby where once the Barnstaple to Lynton Railway had passed by, and ate his fill in the deep shelter of the mill doorway. White feathers caught by the wind blew across the muddy track and under the door of a shed in a stream of brightness in the dark night.

The fox ate on, occasionally glancing about him anxiously as various sounds came to his ears. He ate quickly, knowing not to delay in such places of human habitation for too long. With his meal over he licked his lips and began his journey homewards. The remains of the chicken, freed from Old Red's anchoring forepaws, rolled in a gust of wind to fall into the current of the River Yeo where it swirled to begin its journey to the Taw estuary, passing sheepskin and timber yards, and the tall rectangle of concrete and glass wherein toiled local government officers by day.

Old Red trotted along the lane and over an old plank bridge to come upon a second chicken sheltering under the hedge. This he took in his stride, running faster despite the buffeting of a wing against his face, and rain, which he disliked, beginning to fall steadily once more.

Back on the North Road he swiftly ran to the entrance of Shearford Lane, the sunken route to his valley home. Here he was startled by the sudden appearance of a tawny owl, which had been perched on the old plank seat at the lane head hoping for a mouse or vole to venture forth. Old Red almost dropped the hen as the owl glided silently from the seat to fly close by his head. His strong jaws readjusted his prey and he took the high path along the ancient former pack-horse route in almost total darkness, soaking ferns brushing his coat as he went, the sound of rushing water from flooding fields far below him.

A wood pigeon clattered into the night on loud, stiff wings, disturbed from its holly tree roost, scrabbling clumsily for a new perch in the alien darkness.

Old Red soon reached the lane end, trudging wearily now across the rain-soaked fields his coat clinging to him as he splashed through the pooling water where the stile led into the woods and past the quarry, the track beneath the oaks he knew so well soon taking him to his earth.

A mile or so away at Raleigh hamlet a middle-aged man stretched his legs towards a crackling log fire as his wife handed him a hot drink.

'Did you check the chickens were OK, love?' he asked as she settled opposite him with her own drink.

'Um, er, oh yes, ages ago. It was bucketing with rain when I went out. Had quite a job getting 'em into the run from the garden even though 'twas raining'.

'Awkward little blighters sometimes,' muttered her husband as he sipped his drink, already engrossed in the TV set before them.

Old Red, meanwhile, was asleep with one of the 'awkward little blighters' lying beside him. The next day two chickens would be missed and pondered over, and one day a number of white feathers inside a locked shed would cause further ponderings, but such thoughts are not for foxes.

Of Sparrowhawks and Things

•◆•

Cold, wet winter days are long and hard for most species of wildlife, Old Red often returning hungry to his earth or to the disused badger sett in the woods if the weather was really harsh.

The rain and cold kept small mammals and many birds hidden in whatever shelter they could find, some seeking their caches of nuts and berries laid ready in the autumn. The fox roamed the woodland edges and hedgerows by day as well as by night, ever searching to assuage his hunger. Flocks of tits and finches flitted across the grey-green country-side as he prowled his lone way, at times eating fungi or grubbing up beetles from secret lairs in the leaf litter.

On one bitterly cold afternoon Old Red left the woods to wander to Yarnerwood and beyond, finding himself in the extensive grounds of an old house above Bradiford, hidden amongst trees. He prowled through the shrubbery close to the house and paused, hearing the calls of birds nearby. He padded silently around the house, sheltering in a clump of hydrangeas and rhododendrons, crouching low as a woman came from inside the house to place food scraps upon a bird table. Old Red could scent the food from his hiding place as he watched the woman return indoors, hearing the door slam as she disappeared. Immediately three blue tits alighted on hanging nut-feeders to begin pecking rapidly at the contents. A great tit arrived, then a few greenfinches and the fox saw they were attacking the food just put out. He rose hurriedly and trotting to the bird table he stood on hind legs, eating all there was, bread, cake, cold potato and meat fat, wolfing each morsel and licking the table clean. The birds had scattered, perching about the bushes and lawn, scolding the fox who dropped to all fours to move off around the side of the house once again. As he did so a small, wild-eyed hawk arrived to perch on the fence post nearest the house, its golden eyes staring intently at a number of thrush-like birds which had just arrived in a small flock, singling out one of these as the flock took wing as one. The redwing, one of thousands in the countryside from Scandinavian countries for the winter, left the grass on seeing the sparrowhawk, to fly headlong directly at the house, hotly pursued by the winged predator.

Inside, the woman who had put out the food scraps had observed the fox eating them, marvelling at his beauty, deciding to put out more food as soon as he left. Now she opened the great oak door at the house front as redwing and sparrowhawk headed for the porch in full flight, flashing past her head, the redwing screaming as the hawk behind its head with one outstretched leg bearing needle-sharp talons tore the life from it.

The woman had fallen back against the door in surprise and now she turned in the hallway to see the fierce little hawk busily plucking the feathers from the redwing's breast, half-way up the wooden staircase.

The woman's first reaction was to leap in anger at the hawk and its quarry but then she left the house to walk around the back, hoping the hawk would quickly finish its meal and leave. One hand went up to her mouth to stifle a gasp as there, hunched over a large dish of food placed for her dog, was the fox. He turned his liquid gold eyes on her as both stood warily but the woman did not move. Old Red ate the remainder of the dog food then backed away towards a shed, then turning abruptly he trotted into the bushes and was away towards the woods and his home. The woman watched him as he went then suddenly remembered the sparrowhawk.

'Oh my, what a day!' she exclaimed to herself and ran to enter the house by the back door, whereupon she crept through several rooms to reach the hallway. Upon the red stair carpet was a circle of feathers, the only sign of the two birds that remained. The hawk was gone, flying back towards Tutshill, seeing the fox loping beneath it as they both headed for home and were soon lost amongst the trees.

The End and
a New Beginning

⚫➤⚫

The late winter night was bitterly cold. No wind stirred the frost glinting on blackened twigs at the edge of Tutshill woods, the wet smoothness of beech tree bark reflecting winter moonlight along the lower path of the wood, tree shadows black across the water of the stream which had begun to freeze in its shallowest places.

The only sign that spring was not a hundred years hence was the hazel with its yellow catkins which hung stiffly down from twigs, as yet frost-locked, awaiting the warming rays of the morrow's sun. The lamb's-tail catkins would soon have their pollen tossed by the wind on to the smaller female flowers borne on the same twigs, these in turn forming the cob nuts favoured by squirrels, mice and nuthatches who lived in the woods. To Old Red moving silently towards the small hunting gate leading to the spinney field, the chilled damp woodland was a friendly place, home, the catkins but a wetness brushing his coat as he passed by.

Old Red had eaten well. A hen pheasant had spent the afternoon in the company of two strutting cocks who had crowed and fought along the hedgerow for her favours. Then she had died in her sleep as Old Red prowled, having heard them during the day and knowing the roosting places of the birds, had crept upon them. Finding the two cock birds on a tree branch above the hen, he had killed her before she could utter a sound from her head which she had tucked warmly beneath one wing.

He had eaten where he stood, ignoring the cock pheasants' noisy flight as they swiftly flew into the surrounding darkness, eating hurriedly as if afraid some unseen force might steal his prize. His amber eyes watched the woodland for movement, occasionally closing in the sheer wild enjoyment of his kill. He ate with his lean body hunched, his bushy tail low between his hind legs, the only sound the snap and scrunch of bones and rich meat.

His meal finished, his blood warmed by the food, he licked his lips, a fox's happiness surging through his whole frame, a feeling of well-being coursing through him as he thrust his nose into the dead leaves carpeting the woodland floor to scoop them over the remains of his prey before going on his way. He passed beneath a tree where a raven's nest had been completed that very day, the earliest nest in the valley, built to the sound of the year's first song of a thrush. Trotting out of the wood into the marsh field, Old Red crossed the otter path, swishing through white frosted grasses and the taller clumps of tussock sedge where he followed the stream to a gateway leading into a larger field.

Here on the steep hillside Old Red stood bathed in moonlight, head held sharply back, nose pointing at the star-filled sky and he barked his blood-curdling calls to the great Dog Star, Sirius, shining brighter than any other above the black and silver landscape.

Old Red barked again, the eerie, screaming cry carrying far into the frost-filled stillness of the night as field mice and voles huddled trembling in their holes. The moon, high now, cast its bright light upon the earth as the Dog Star twinkled, turning from red to emerald, its reflection in the stream below glittering in the icy water shallows.

From the opposite hillside where the valley slopes wandered to Blakewell and beyond, came the echoing call of another fox and Old Red sprang about, every sense alert, ears erect and pointing forward to trap every sound, eyes staring, straining across the fields where every tree stood starkly clear in the moonlight.

All was silent now save for the chattering of the stream. Old Red's eyes caught no movement other than water glints. He moved a dozen paces down over the slope, standing in the shadows of gorse, becoming part of the shadows, invisible and silent.

Some sixth sense, known to all wild creatures, told him of a presence. His hackles rose, his tail stiffening as he watched the scene before him. The field here swept steeply down to the water's edge, the smooth slope broken by scattered gorse and bramble, the black shadows of which lay downwards towards the stream. Along the waterway grew many alders with ash trees spaced sentinel-like along its length to where a clump of birch trees stood silvery over short grass, amongst which grew fly agaric toadstools each autumn. Here were two gateways, one with a five-barred gate leading out towards Blakewell, the other with a narrow hunting gate leading into a neglected apple orchard scrumped by many a town and country child when the fly agaric was at its best.

Old Red's eyes stared unblinking where both gateways showed brightly visible but naught moved. Or did it? The fox stared harder, raising himself to his full height, whining quietly in his excitement though he did not know why.

The night had grown colder, shallow water in the orchard gateway suddenly freezing solid where the hooves of cattle had impressed the soil days before. Into the field from the gateway stepped a fox, a vixen born in the spring before himself, at Muddiford in a quarry earth. Old Red watched her glance along the footpath towards the woods and then follow it, walking slowly.

He called to her in the way of his kind, trotting diagonally down across the hill slope to stop close in front of her tensed body.

For long moments the two foxes faced each other on the pathway, Old Red in his own known territory, the vixen exploring pastures new, for she was Grey Fleck from the fields and woods of Ashford by the Taw, and she had wandered far since her sickness from man's pollution had almost killed her.

Old Red stood his ground, every sense alert, eyes staring into her eyes, and he whined again in his excitement, barking once, a short, sharp bark of greeting, half remembering her scent from somewhere deep in his memory.

The vixen edged slowly forward, placing a forepaw close to him and stretching her neck she touched her nose to his. She was lonely and had wandered aimlessly for days from Milltown where her mate lay choked by a wire snare several miles away.

They had fought the terrible choking snare together, he pulling back until his ears were dragged forward and bleeding over his staring eyes by the ever tightening wire noose, and she until her white upper lip bled freely, her white chin and throat fur red with her own blood as she bit at the wire noose in a frenzy of fear and hatred. Her mate's anger had turned to cold fear as he found no escape from the snare and he had lain whimpering, his pain-racked body gasping and heaving on the hedge bank, held fast by the wire of death attached tightly to hawthorn roots. He last saw his mate through a mist as she tried to lick life into his once handsome face and then she was no longer in his vision though his eyes were wide open.

She had left him then where he lay, staring sightlessly after her and for the rest of that night, and the next day and night, she had wandered aimlessly across many fields and along lanes and wood edges where the dawn had bade her sleep in the old churchyard at Shirwell. She had slept fitfully, then rose to kill a starving rat, then walked on again, lost.

Now she stood before Old Red. He licked her face as they touched noses, welcoming her to his life, their breaths mingling, joy filling their bodies. Grey Fleck licked Old Red's face and turned away to run up over the slope with new found vigour, Old Red catching her, leaping to nip her in play, barking with the sound of a jay harsh in his throat, she answering with the same jay-like cry as she followed him.

They ran the length of the field together, romping and playing, leaping at each other's bodies in their mutual joy, the vixen suddenly alive to this dog fox and he suddenly alive to his every instinct for he had found his mate. They took pleasure in each other, howling together at the moon, the trees and the world in the joy of togetherness. Their romping led them to the gateway by the spinney at the bottom of the hill slope where they mated again then faced each other panting. The vixen whined at Old Red then and he knew she was hungry.

He led his mate into the marsh field and beyond to where he quickly found the remains of his recent pheasant meal. Grey Fleck fell upon it ravenously, Old Red watching her eat her fill, standing away to one side, occasionally whining in his new-found excitement. Only once did she look up, growling in her throat but there was no anger in her, only the deep joy of wild creatures in each other. The pheasant now but a few bones and feathers adhering to frosted leaves, the vixen turned away to follow Old Red into the woods where the dawn and a rising sun found them huddled warmly together in Old Red's earth.

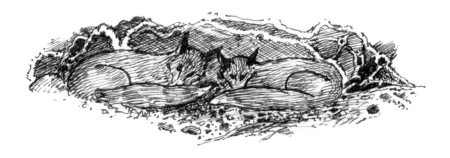

THE END

About the Fox

·◆·

The red fox (*Vulpes vulpes*) is a common animal of the British country-side and is smaller than most people imagine, being usually about 2ft (61cm) in length with a bushy, white-tipped tail of a further 16ins (400mm). They stand about 14ins (350mm) at the shoulder and have beautiful fur of a russet, red-brown or sandy colour with much variation. The underparts are white.

The weight of an average dog fox is around 15lbs (6.8kg), a vixen 12lbs (5.4kg). The fox's description needs little said about it, the sharp-pointed long muzzle and erect pointed ears being well known. A healthy fox always appears alert, the eyes bright or quick moving. Dog foxes and vixens are similar in appearance though the vixen lacks the cheek ruffs of the male and thus appears narrower of face. I have seen foxes with black tips to the tail and several black foxes (melanistic) but these are few and far between.

The fox's survival is due to its high intelligence. When eluding man it is an extremely clever animal, which of course, it has to be. Some say that but for the Hunt the fox would be extinct or nearly so. This is highly unlikely though it is true the fox is relatively 'safe' in hunting country except when actually being hunted, though it has to be said that many are shot each year.

Foxes have five digits on the forefeet, four on the hind, though prints in mud, snow or sand or the like, only show four in contact with the ground. Fox tracks show in a much straighter line than do dog tracks, often the hind feet overprinting those of the forefeet which occasionally gives the impression of a five-digit print.

Fox-runs through a hedge are smaller than those of a badger and larger than a hare's without the jump pattern of the latter. The most frequent gait is a trot of about 6-10 km per hour and the animal swims very well.

It is difficult to quote the range or territory of a fox with any accuracy, the richer the habitat the smaller the range and obviously a fox will increase its range when food is scarce, irrespective of 'boundaries' or other foxes. Scent marking by urine on territories is the fox's method of establishing his or her presence and the secretions from the perianal glands are also used.

Foxes are mainly nocturnal and crepuscular but are often about during daylight hours in the autumn and winter and on late summer nights before sundown. I have met with many foxes well into the hours of mid-morning in secluded countryside at all times of the year. Quite obviously their activity is affected by our own and they avoid humans wherever possible.

The fox is mainly a surface-dwelling animal and though nocturnal activity is not strictly influenced by weather conditions they will readily shelter from inclement weather, seeking underground refuge (e.g., old badger setts) when rainfall is prolonged or there is much snow. The preference for underground habitat is also evident during the cubbing season when the well-known earths are used. Many foxes live most of the time in their earths, which usually have two entrance or exit holes.

The earths described in the *Old Red* story are typical of those in my home area, foxes often excavating their own earths. On Exmoor I have found earths dug cleverly into the heather hillsides beneath rocky crags or outcrops. Foxes will readily take old rabbit burrows or disused badger setts, holes under fallen trees in woods or hedgerows and under brambles or gorse in quarries or on coastal cliffs.

Foxes have a high-pitched bark, usually uttered in groups of two to four at a time and also a wailing bark, which is less common. Normally they call for the few hours after sunset and much less often in the early hours of the day. The breeding season screaming is a weird sound often interspersed with the jay-like call referred to in the last chapter of *Old Red*.

Foxes appear to prefer voles to mice, which may reflect preference plus ease of capture for field voles are the most commonly taken. Many rabbits are taken, as are rats and earthworms. One farmer I chatted to stated that he 'relied on' a fox, living locally, to keep down the rat population at his smallholding.

In summer many insects are consumed, as are fruit and berries in summer and autumn, blackberries being popular and fungi too are commonly eaten. Lambs are usually only taken when less than 24 hours old and one of twins, reflecting the ease of capture of such prey. Nowadays, with the modern methods of poultry-keeping, foxes take far less poultry though ducks and geese ranging free are still an easy target. Colonial nesting birds are also taken, as are sheep and cattle afterbirths, and the edible contents of refuse bins in urban areas.

Foxes commonly cache food surplus to their immediate requirements and such caches are often easily observable. A fox requires about 500 grams of food daily.

Young are usually born in spring with four or five cubs to a litter – only a single litter per year. Mating takes place night or day and the pair may be locked in coitus for up to half an hour. Females have a single oestrous period of three weeks but fertilisation is only possible for three days.

The gestation period is 52–53 days. Lactation lasts for about six weeks and cubs are blind at birth, though covered in fur. The vixen remains with the cubs during the day and much of the night for the first three weeks and then usually lies up elsewhere during the day. Males occasionally bring food to the vixen during the period immediately following parturition. At about 4–5 weeks the cubs begin weaning to regurgitated food and are fully weaned at 6–7 weeks.

Fox Watching

·◆·

Watching foxes is not the easiest aspect of natural history to pursue, mainly because they are extremely wary animals and are not always about where one expects, or hopes for, them to be.

Badgers, for example, can normally be observed at their setts all the year round but foxes can only be found with certainty at particular times of the year. Cubs, for example, are pretty well tied to the den for a long time and I have found May and June are the ideal months to see them playing, especially in the hours before sunset.

When they are very small the vixen lies with them and this is one of the finest sights in nature, a vixen and her cubs at play. It is also likely as the cubs get a little older that one may see both dog and vixen bringing food to the den. The most common den type is the enlarged rabbit burrow, the soft soil or sand being easy digging for the adult fox.

The strong, musky odour of the fox is well known and is a giveaway when checking a den or earth for current use. Tracks too are helpful but beware of dog tracks at such sites, many dogs wandering the countryside being attracted to nose about and leave their own prints. Thus the prey of the fox, left about the den or earth is the surest way of knowing the animal is about. When prey is plentiful there may well be an abundance of items lying around; feathers, wings, beaks and claws, bones and rabbits' feet, for example, but when food is short the remains will be fewer. If the food is mainly small mammals the cubs will devour the entire animal and thus few if any traces will remain. It is, therefore, a fact of life that foxes, though so cunningly wary when about the countryside, are nevertheless, somewhat careless, by comparison, when advertising their presence at home. Fox scats, too, will be found about the area, foxes not digging latrines as do badgers.

Vixens may move their cubs at any invasion of their privacy so all I would say to the would-be fox watcher is respect that privacy and watch and delight in the sight of such animals from a distance. Careful stalking within viewing distance is all that is necessary to observe wild animals – otherwise leave well alone. Remember too that whilst young cubs are more tolerant and may be fooled, this does not apply to the vixen who is very much aware of all that goes on about her youngsters. The vixen approaches with the wind in or to the side of her face, knowing all that lies ahead of her!

The best way to observe cubs is, therefore, to get off the ground, say before sunrise, and await events with patience. If you haven't any patience then animal watching is not for you. It is likely at this time of day that the vixen will approach the den with food for the cubs and thus if you are not off the ground or at some distant viewpoint she will locate you easily enough. The vixen will then bark a warning to her cubs who will either remain below ground or, if they are out and about, will immediately bolt below. Once the cubs are alerted to the association of the vixen's bark and your scent or visual presence, they will henceforth associate you with danger and no further warning bark will be needed to send them packing. As the cubs grow older more care is needed in watching and by June they must be treated as adult foxes anyway, so sharp are their senses. I have been located at 100 metres even when taking, as I thought, immense care, the slightest movement making a vixen with cubs suspicious. If you feel you may be being observed by a fox then freeze, making no movement whatever even if you are looking through a binocular; just remain very still and hope you do not upset her.

Remember there is no need to move closer than 50 metres to see foxes and at closer distance you are more likely to disturb them and therefore will see little or nothing, a pointless exercise. Vixens are excellent mothers and dog foxes good fathers, the latter rearing the cubs if the vixen has been killed provided they have been weaned and are able to take the prey he brings. A vixen will risk her life to save her cubs as in the *Old Red* story.

Also in the story, two youngsters use a red-filtered torch to observe wildlife at night. This does work perfectly well and foxes and badgers certainly do not seem to see red light. White light used in this way is of little use and you will scare away your fox. White light is only of use if it is left on all the time and the animal is allowed to get used to it over periods of time – in its own time.

Foxes do not hunt in packs but may well gather at large carcasses, say a dead stag or whatever, which has died or been killed by some other means.

And so – enjoy your mammal watching keeping one thing uppermost in your mind – let the animal enjoy it too!

Take nothing but pictures
Leave nothing but footprints
Kill nothing but time.